Contemporary Classics

100 Favorites for Voice and
Easy Piano

Compiled by Ken Bible
Arrangements by Ken Thomas

Lillenas Publishing Co.
KANSAS CITY, MO. 64141

Praise the Lord, He Never Changes

STORMIE SHERRIC

RON HARRIS

A9sus
A13
D sus
D
3
one.
way.
Praise the Lord,
He nev - er
Gm
C7
Gm sus
G♭7
chang - es;
I come to Him,
He's al - ways
F
F6
Em9♯
A9
there.
He com - forts me on
Dm7
Dm7/C
Dm6/B
D/E
E
ev - 'ry lev - el,
Takes the bur - dens that I
A9sus
A
D sus
D
3
bear.
Praise the Lord,
He nev - er

Gm
C7
Gm7
G♭7
chang - es; He's nev - er an - y oth - er
F
F+/A
B♭M7
Am7
way. And He'll be the same to -
Gm7sus
Am7
B♭M7
G9/B
C7sus
mor - row As He was and is to -
F
B♭/F
1st time: repeat
2nd time: go on
day.
F
B♭add9/F
F
rit.
8va

I Go to the Rock

D. R.

DOTTIE RAMBO

C7 C7sus C7 B♭ Gm7 B♭/F F
Rock of my sal - va - tion, go to the Stone that the build-ers re - ject - ed; Run to the
Dm Am B♭ G7/B C7sus C7 B♭/C C7
moun - tain and the moun - tain stands by me. The earth all a -
F C7/G F/A F/C A7/C♯ A7/E Dm F/C B♭ Gm7
round me is sink-ing sand; on Christ, the sol - id Rock, I stand. When I need a
F D7 G9 C7 1 F7/A Gm7 F
shel - ter, when I need a friend I go to the Rock. 2. Where do I
2 F7/A Gm7 F F7/A Gm7 F
Rock.

I'd Rather Have Jesus

RHEA F. MILLER

GEORGE BEVERLY SHEA

REFRAIN
Dm9 G7 C G Dm7 G
nail - pierced hand
ho - ly name
let Him lead
Than to be the king of a
F/A F C G Dm7 G
vast do - main Or be held in sin's dread
F/C C C C7
sway! I'd rath - er have Je - sus than
F C Am6 C/G G F/G
an - y - thing This world af - fords to -
1,2 C F/G 3 C F/C C
day. 2. I'd 3. He's day.

The Blood Will Never Lose Its Power

A. C.

ANDRAE CROUCH

Eb7
Db/F
Eb/G
Ab
Db/Ab
Ab7
flows to the low - est val - ley. The
Db
D°
Ab/Eb
Ab/Gb
F7
blood that gives me strength from day to day, It will
Bbm
F7/C
Bbm7/Db
Fm/D
Eb7
Ab
Db/Ab
1
Ab
nev - er lose its pow'r. 2. It
2
Ab
F7/A
Bbm
F7/C
Bbm7/Db
Bbm
F7/C
Bbm7/Db
Fm/D
It will nev - er, nev - er lose
Eb7
Ab
Db/Ab
Ab
its pow'r.

Sail On

C. C.

CHRIS CHRISTIAN

F
B♭
F
Then when we find out to Him we be-long, We watch for the signs and
Just keep your com - pass set on the Son; He'll guide you safe - ly to His
1
C7
F
keep sail - in' on. Sail on
2
C7
F
beau-ti - ful home.
B♭
We can't af - ford to
F/A
Gm7
C7
F
throw our lives to the wind;
B♭
F
Gm
Am
We've got the Lord in con - trol of our ship, and He'll guide us safe - ly
C9
D.S.
CODA
F
in. Sail on
R.H.

Peace in the Midst of the Storm

S. R. A.

STEPHEN R. ADAMS

Eb Ab Eb Eb9

peace in the midst of my storm - tossed life; Oh, there's an

Ab Fm7 Bb9sus Bb7

an - chor, there's a rock to cast my faith up - on. Je - sus

Eb Eb7/Db Bbm7/Db Eb7 Ab Cm/A Ao

rides in my ves - sel so I'll fear no a - larm; He gives me

Eb/Bb 1,2 Gm/Bb Bb7 Eb

peace in the midst of my storm!

2. When in
3. When my

3 Gm/Bb Bb7 Eb F/Eb Ab/Eb Bb7 Eb

midst of the storm. The midst of the storm.

We Shall Behold Him

D. R.

DOTTIE RAMBO

Db Db Gb/Ab Db Db7 Gb Ab/Gb
face. We shall be - hold Him; we shall be
face.
Db/F Db Gb Db/F Db/F Gb G° Db/Ab Ab
hold Him Face to face in all of His glo - ry.
Gb/Ab Db Gb Ab/Gb
We shall be - hold Him; we shall be -
Db/F Db Gb Db/F Ebm/Ab Db/Ab Ab7
hold Him Face to face, our Sav - ior and
1 Db
Lord. 2. The
2 Db
Lord.

Mountain Top

B. B.

BROWN BANNISTER

G M7 G6 B sus B7 Em Em/D
moun-tain top, fel - low - ship - ping with the Lord.
Am7 C/D G M7 G6 A7
I'd love to stand on a moun-tain top 'cause I love to feel my spir - it
Legato
Am7 D7 Am7 C/D G M7 G6
soar; But I've got to come down from the moun-tain top to the
Detached
B sus B7 Em Em/D C B sus B7
peo - ple in the val - ley be - low. Or they'll nev - er know that
Em D C G/B Am7 D7 G
3rd time to Coda
they can go to the moun-tain of the Lord.

Am/G
1 G
2. Now
2 G
G
Am/D
3. Now I am not say - ing that wor - ship is wrong, But
G/D
G
wor-ship is more than just sing - ing a song; It's all that you say and ev - 'ry -
Am/D
G/D
D7 G
D.S. al Coda
thing that you do. It's let-ting His Spir - it live through you. But I'd
CODA
Am/G
G

Eternal Life

St. FRANCIS of ASSISI

OLIVE DUNGAN

A/C♯ Dm Fm6/A♭ C/G A/G
seek To be con - soled as to con - sole, To be
G7sus G7 C
un - der - stood as to un - der - stand, To be loved as to
Am Fm6/A♭ C/G
cresc. poco a poco
love. For it is in giv - ing that
Fm6 C/E F6
we re - ceive; It is in
D/F♯ F D/F♯ C/G C+/G♯
par - doning that we are par - doned; It is in

Am
Dm7 5b
C6/G
G9b 7
dy - ing that we are born to e - ter - nal
rit.
ff
C
Am
F
Fm
C
a tempo
life!
rit.
p
Cornerstone
L. G.
LARI GOSS
Ab
Db/Ab
Ab
Bbm/Ab
Je - sus
Ab
Cm7/G
Fm
Bbmsus
Eb7
is the Cor-ner - stone, Came for sin - ners to a -
am by sin op - pressed, On the Stone I am at
Ab
Cm7/G
Fm
Fm/Eb
Bb/D
Bb7
Eb
Eo
tone. Tho' re - ject - ed by His own, He be - came the Cor-ner-
rest. When the seeds of truth are sown, He re - mains the Cor-ner-

1
2
Fm Fm/Eb D°
Ab/Eb
Eb7sus Eb7
Eb E°
stone; Je - sus is the Cor-ner - stone. When I
stone; Je - sus is the Cor-ner- stone.
F
Bb/F
F
Bb/F
Rock of
F FM7
F7 Bb/F
F C/E
Cm/Eb Bb/D Bbm6/Db
A - ges, cleft for me, Let me
F/C
Dm6/B Bb/C C7
F
F+/A
hide my - self in Thee. Rock of
Dm
G7
C G6/B
Am
A - ges, so se - cure, For all time it shall en - dure. 'Til His

Dm G7 C F E7sus
chil-dren reach their home, He re-mains the Cor-ner-stone.
E D/E E A C♯m7/G♯ F♯m E7sus/B E7
'Til the break-ing of the dawn, 'Til all foot-steps cease to
A C♯m7/G♯ F♯m F♯m/E B/D♯ B7 E C♯/E♯
roam, Ev-er let this truth be known: Je-sus is the Cor-ner-
F♯m F♯m/E F♯m/D♯ A/E F♯m Bm7 D/E
stone. Je-sus is the Cor-ner-
A G/A D/A A
stone.

Rise Again

D. H.

DALLAS HOLM

3rd time to Coda
Db
Bbm7
Eb
Ab/Eb Eb
Ab
Db/Ab
gain;
Death can't keep Me in the ground.
gain;
Come to take My peo - ple
Eb/Ab
Ab
Ab
Bb/Ab
p
2. Go a - head and mock My name, My
3. Go a - head and say I'm dead and gone, But
Db/Ab
Ab
Absus
Ab
love for you is still the same. Go a - head and
you will see that you were wrong. Go a - head and
Bb/Ab
Db/Ab
Ab
Db/Ab
Ab
D.S. twice
bur - y Me, But ver - y soon I will be free. 'Cause I'll
try to hide the Son, But all will see that I'm the One! 'Cause I'll
CODA
Ab
Db/Ab
Eb/Ab
Ab
back!
p

More of You

GLORIA GAITHER

WILLIAM J. GAITHER & GARY S. PAXTON

B♭
B♭7
E♭
G7/D
Cm
Cm/B♭
You, more of You; I've had
F7
F7/C
Cm7
E♭/F F13
F9
B♭
F13
all, but what I need just more of You. Of things I've
E♭/B♭
B♭
B♭9
E♭
G7/D
had my fill and yet I hun - ger still;
Cm
Cm7
F
Cm7
F7
Emp - ty and bare; Lord, hear my prayer for more of
1
B♭
Cm/B♭
B♭M7
Cm/B♭
B♭
F13
2
B♭
Cm/B♭
B♭M7
Cm/B♭
E♭m6/B♭
B♭
You. 2. I have You.

M. L.

His Grace Is Sufficient for Me

MOSIE LISTER
Arr. by Ken Thomas

Db Ab F7 Bb7 Eb9 Ab Db/Ab

Ab Eb7 Ab Db/Ab Ab Eb7 Ab Eb7

1. Man - y times I'm tried and test - ed as I trav - el day by
temp - ter brings con - fu - sion and I don't know what to

Ab Eb Eb7 Ab Db/Ab

day; Oft I meet with pain and sor - row, and there's trou - ble in the
do, On my knees I turn to Je - sus, for I know He'll see me

Ab Eb7 Ab Db/Ab Ab Eb7 Ab C7

way. But I have the sweet as - sur - ance that my soul the Lord will
through. Then de - spair is changed to vic - t'ry, ev - 'ry doubt just melts a -

Fm Db Ab F7 Bb7 Eb9 Ab Db/Ab

lead, And in Him there is strength for ev - 'ry need. ______
way; And in Him there is hope for ev - 'ry day. ______

REFRAIN
Ab
Eb
Db
Ab
Db/Ab
Oh, His grace is suf - fi - cient for me,
Ab
Eb
Db
Ab
Db/Ab
And His love is a - bun - dant and free;
Ab
C7
And what joy fills my soul just to know, just to
Fm
Db
Ab
F7
Bb7
Eb9
1
Ab
Db/Ab
know That His grace is suf - fi - cient for me.
Ab
Eb7
2
Ab
Db/Ab
Ab
2. When the me.

Sheltered in the Arms of God

D. R. and J. D.

DOTTIE RAMBO and JIMMY DAVIS

CHORUS
Ab
Db
Ab
Eb
So let the storms rage high, the dark clouds rise; they won't wor-ry
Ab
C7/G
Fm
Ab/Eb
Bb9/D
Bb9
Bbm7
me, For I'm shel - tered safe with - in the arms of God.
Eb
Ab
Ab7
Db
Ab
He walks with me, and naught of earth shall harm me,
AbM7/C
B°
Bbm7
Eb7
1
Ab
Db/Ab
For I'm shel - tered in the arms of God.
2
Ab
Db/Ab
Ab
Db/Ab
Ab
God.

Peace in the Valley

T. A. D.

THOMAS A. DORSEY

B♭ F/A F Am7

peace in the val - ley for me some - day; There'll be

Dm G7 C C7

peace in the val - ley for me, I pray. No more

F F7 E♭/G F7/A B♭ G7 B° F/C Dm

sor - row and sad - ness or trou-ble will be; There'll be peace in the

G7 C7 1 F B♭/F B♭m/F F 2 F B♭ B°

val - ley for me. 2. There the me.

Even 8ths

F/C Dm G7 C7 F B♭/F B♭m/F F

Great and Wonderful

S. D.

STUART DAUERMANN
Arr. by Ken Thomas

Dm
D7
Gm
Thou.
Who
shall
not
Dm
Gm
fear
and
glo - ri - fy
Thy
name,
O
Dm
Gm
Lord?
For
Thou
a -
Dm
Gm
lone
art
ho - ly,
Thou
a -
A
D.S. al Coda
CODA
Dm
lone.
men.

I Should Have Been Crucified

G. J.

GORDON JENSEN

C7 F/C C7 Cm7 F7 F
go; take Me in - stead." And
took them and let me go free!
CHORUS
Bb F7 Bb Bb7 Eb
I should have been cru - ci - fied; I should have
Bb Cm7sus F7 Bb Bb/D F/C Bb7
suf - fered and died! I should have hung on the
Eb C7 Bb/F Cm7 F7
cross in dis - grace; But Je - sus, God's Son, took my
1 Bb F7sus/C F7sus F
place! 2. Crown of
2 Bb
place!

He Was There All the Time

G. S. P. GARY S. PAXTON

Dm Bb G7/B G7
in; And all the while Some-one was beg-ging to free me from
life; But, O what I missed—He'd been wait-ing right there all the
C G13 C Em7 F Dm7
sin!
time! He was there all the time; He was
G7 C G7 C Em7
there all the time, Wait-ing pa-tient-ly in
F Fm6 C/G G13 1 C
line. He was there all the time!
2 C Fm6 C
time! rit.

Home Where I Belong

P. T.

PAT TERRY

4th time to Coda

Bbsus Bb7 Ab

where I __ be-long. ____

Eb

1,3

2

Ab

While I'm here I'll serve

G7sus G7 Cm Ab

__ Him glad - ly and sing Him all these songs. ______ I'm here

Eb Bb7sus Bb D.S.

but not for long. ______

CODA

Ab Eb

Only Jesus Can Satisfy Your Soul

L. W.

LANNY WOLFE

Eb7/Ab Ab Db9 Eb G7 Cm Cm/Bb
Je - sus can sat - is - fy your soul; And on - ly
F9/A F7 Fm Bb7
He can change your heart and make you whole. He'll give you
Eb EbM7 Bbm7 Eb7 Ab Db9
peace you nev-er knew, sweet love and joy and heav-en, too; For on-ly
Eb Cm Fm7 Bb9 1 Eb Ab/Eb Eb Ab/Bb Bb
Je - sus can sat - is - fy your soul. 2. If you could
2 EM7 Db9 Ab/Bb Abm/Bb Eb
soul.

Now Walk with God

C G9sus Dm7/G A♭o Gm11
do. And may your life re -
C7/G Gm7 C7 F F6 Am6/F B/D D♯o
flect His love to ev - 'ry - one. Now walk with
C/E C♯o Dm Dm7 Dm9/G G7 1 C
God and He will walk with you.
2 Em11 A9 G♯7 A7 Dm11
you. Now walk with God and
Dm7 Dm9/G G7 C D♭M7 C6/9
He will walk with you.
rit.
8va

Greater Is He That Is in Me

L. W. LANNY WOLFE

B♭ C7 C9sus C7
Seek - ing whom he may de - vour— the Bi - ble tells us
Blew in - to the up - per room and bap - tized all of
F Gm
so. Man - y souls have been his prey to
them With a pow - er great - er than
C7 C9sus C7 F
fall in some weak hour; But God has prom - ised
an - y earth - ly foe. And I'm so glad I've
Gm C C9sus C7 F
D.S. twice
us to - day His o - ver - com - ing pow'r.
got it, too; I'll let the whole world know.
CODA
F C9 C9sus C7 F
world.

My Tribute

A. C.

ANDRAE CROUCH

B♭ Dm7 G Cm E♭m6 F
God be the glo - ry; To God be the glo - ry; To
D D7 Gm Gm/F C9/E F9sus F
God be the glo - ry for the things He has done. With His
B♭ Dm7 G7 Cm E♭m6 F F/E♭
blood He has saved me; With His pow'r He has raised me. To
3 3 3
D D9 Gm C7/E B♭/F E♭/F B♭
God be the glo - ry for the things He has done. Just let me
3
Amsus D7/A Gm Gm7♯ Gm7 C9/G
live my life; let it be pleas - ing, Lord, to Thee; And should I

E♭
Gm
C7
Cm7
F7/C
gain any - y praise, let it go to Cal - va - ry. With His
B♭
Dm7
G7
Cm
E♭m
F
F/E♭
blood He has saved me; With His pow'r He has raised me. To
D
D7
Gmsus
C7/E
B♭/F
Cm7/F
B♭
God be the glo - ry for the things He has done. For the
Gm
G♭+
B♭/F
E♭/F
rit.
things, for the things, for the things He has
a tempo
B♭
F/A
B♭/A♭
E♭M7/G
E♭/F
B♭
done.
rit.

Take My Hand, Precious Lord

T. A. D.

THOMAS A. DORSEY

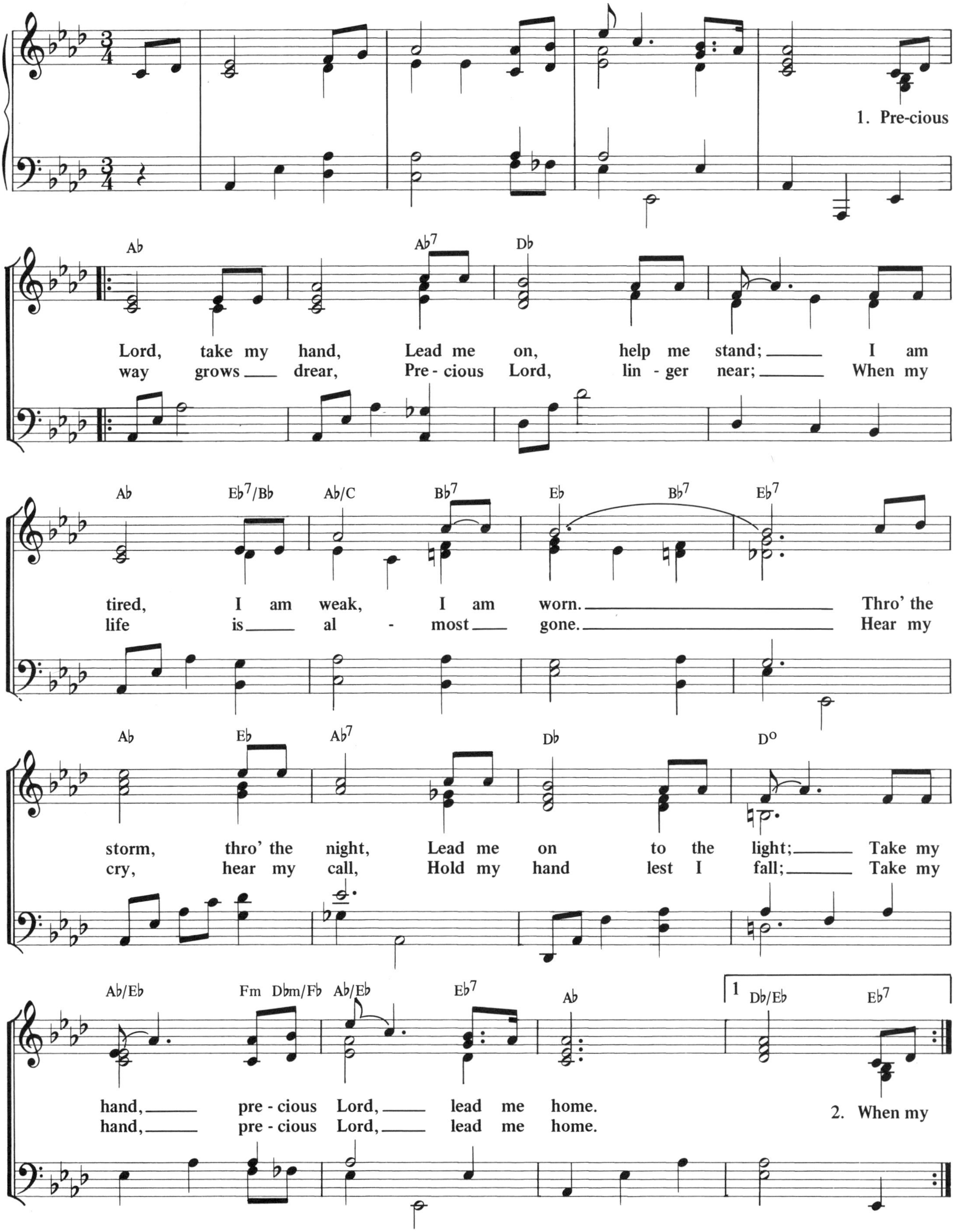
1. Pre-cious
Ab Ab7 Db
Lord, take my hand, Lead me on, help me stand; I am
way grows drear, Pre - cious Lord, lin - ger near; When my
Ab Eb7/Bb Ab/C Bb7 Eb Bb7 Eb7
tired, I am weak, I am worn. Thro' the
life is al - most gone. Hear my
Ab Eb Ab7 Db D°
storm, thro' the night, Lead me on to the light; Take my
cry, hear my call, Hold my hand lest I fall; Take my
Ab/Eb Fm Dbm/Fb Ab/Eb Eb7 Ab 1 Db/Eb Eb7
hand, pre - cious Lord, lead me home.
hand, pre - cious Lord, lead me home.
2. When my

Thou Art Worthy

Rev. 4:11

PAULINE MICHAEL MILLS

Eb Db/Eb Eb7 Ab Db/Ab

Ab Ab7 Db Do

Thou art wor - thy, Thou art wor - thy,

Ab/Eb Fm Db6 Eb

Thou art wor - thy, O Lord,

Ab Ab7 Db Do
To re - ceive glo - ry, glo - ry and hon - or,
Ab/Eb Eb Db/Eb Eb7 Ab Eb
Glo - ry and hon - or and power. For Thou hast cre -
Db/Eb Eb7 Ab Absus Ab Eb Db/Eb Eb7
a - ted, hast all things cre - a - ted; Thou hast cre - a - ted all
Ab Ab7 Db
things. And for Thy plea - sure they are cre -
Do Ab/Eb Eb Db/Eb Eb Ab
a - ted, For Thou art wor - thy, O Lord.

Old Man's Rubble

B. B.

BROWN BANNISTER

Ab/Eb
Eb
know that's bad ___ for your spir - i - tual health.
feel that some-thing's got a - hold ___ of you?
And are you try - in' to live ___
Well, deep with-in you there's a
Ab/Eb
Eb
F/Eb
Bb
___ by your e-mo-tions? Are you put - ting your faith ___ in what you feel and see?
spir - i - tual bat-tle. There's a voice of the dark - ness and a voice of light;
Eb
Ab/Eb
Eb
Then you're liv-in' just to sat - is - fy your passions, And you bet - ter be care - ful 'cause you're
And just by list-'nin' you've made a de - ci - sion 'Cause the voice ___ you ___ hear is gon-na
Ab/Eb
Eb
Ab/Eb
Eb
Bb/Eb
Eb
be - in' de - ceived.
win ___ the fight.
Are you liv - in' in an old man's rub-ble? Are you
Ab/Eb
Eb
Bb/Eb
Eb
Ab/Eb
Eb
lis - ten - in' to the fa - ther of lies?
If you are, then you're

Bb/Eb Eb Ab/Eb Eb Bb/Eb 2nd time to Coda Eb
head-ed for trou - ble. If you lis-ten too long, you'll e - ven-tual-ly die.
Bb/F F C/F F Bb/F F C/F
Are you liv-in' in an old man's rub-ble? Are you lis-ten-in' to the fa-
F Bb/F F C/F F
- ther of lies? If you are, then you're head-ed for trou - ble. If you
Bb/F F C/F F Fm7/Bb D.S. al Coda
lis-ten too long, you'll e - ven-tual-ly die.
CODA Bb/F F C/F F Bb/F F
p
If you're liv - in' as a new cre - a - tion, If you're lis-ten-in' to the Fa-

C/F
F
Bb/F
F
C/F
F
- ther of Light, Then you're liv - in' in a might - y for - tress, And you're
Bb/F
F
C/F
F
f
Bb/F
F
gon - na be clothed in pow - er and light. Are you liv - in' in an
C/F
F
Bb/F
F
C/F
F
old man's rub - ble? Are you lis - ten - in' to the fa - ther of lies?
Bb/F
F
C/F
F
Bb/F
F
C/F
If you are, then you're head-ed for trou - ble. If you lis-ten too long you'll e - ven-tual-ly
F
Bb/F
F
C/F
F
die.

Nobody Cared

J. H.

JACK HAYFORD
Arr. by Ken Thomas

2
C
F
Dm6
Em
cared. But, oh, how the thou-sands came when the bread was mul - ti -
Am
F
Dm6
Em
plied! And, oh, how the ho - san - nas rang at their King's tri - um-phal
C7
F
G7/F
E7
E7/G♯
ride! And as long as the mir - a - cles flowed like
Am
F
Em
Dm11
G
D.S. al Coda
wine, They called Him won-der-ful; they came to dine. 3. But
CODA
C
C/G
D9/F♯
F M7/G
C
cared.
rit.

More
(Than You'll Ever Know)

P. J.

PHIL JOHNSON

C6 C7 F Dm7 CM7 G7sus G7
know. Christ means more to me than I could pos-si-bly show!
C C9/Bb F/A Bb9 C/G
More, more, so much more, More than you'll
G7sus G7 1 C F6/C 2 C F/C
ev - er know. 2. If know!
C C9/Bb F/A Bb9 C/G
more, more, so much more, More than you'll
F/G G13 C F/C F/G C
ev - er know!
L.H.

Love Was When

JOHN E. WALVOORD

DON WYRTZEN

Eb Ab/Bb Bb7 Eb Bb13

Eb Ab/Eb Eb F/Eb

1. Love was when God be - came a man,
2. Love was when God be - came a man

Bb/D Cm7 Bb7 Eb

Locked in time and space with - out rank or place.
Down where I could see, love that reached to me.

Bb7sus Bb7 Eb Ab/Eb Eb F/Eb

Love was God born of Jew - ish kin,
Love was God dy - ing for my sin;

Bb/D Cm7 Bb7 Eb

Just a car - pen-ter with some fish - er - men.
And so trapped was I my whole world caved in.

Eb7
Ab
Bb/Ab
Bb/D
Gm
Love was when Je-sus walked in his - to-ry;
Love was when Je-sus rose to walk with me;
C7
Fm
Fm/Eb
Bb7
Bb7/Ab
G7sus
G7
Lov-ing-ly He brought a new life that's free.
Lov-ing-ly He brought a new life that's free.
AbM7
Bb7
Eb
Ab/Eb
Eb
Love was God nailed to
Love was God; on - ly
F/Eb
Bb/D
Cm7
Bb7sus
Bb7
bleed and die, To reach and love one such as
He would try To reach and love one such as
1
Eb
Bb13
I.
2
Eb
Ab/Eb
Bb/Eb
Eb
I.

V. E.

VEP ELLIS
Arr. by Ken Thomas

Eb/Bb Bb9 Bb7 Eb Bb13

1. Let me

Eb Ab/Eb Ab7/Eb Eb

touch Him; let me touch Je - sus. Let me
stray - ing so far from Je - sus. I was

Bb Bbsus Bb7

touch Him as He pass - es by. Then when
lone - ly, had no peace with - in. Then the

8va

Eb Ab/Eb Eb

I shall reach out to oth - ers, They shall
hand of my Sav - ior touched me; Now I'm

Eb/Bb Bb9 Bb7 Eb Ab/Eb Eb CHORUS

know Him; they shall live and not die.
reach-ing to oth - ers in sin. Oh, to

Bb7
Eb
be His hand ex - tend - ed,
Reach-ing
Bb
Eb
Eb7
out to the op - pressed!
Let me
Ab
Ab7/Eb
Eb
touch Him; let me touch Je - sus
So that
Eb/Bb
Bb9
Bb7
1
Eb
Ab/Eb
Bb13
oth - ers may know and be blessed.
2. I was
2
Eb
Ab/Eb
Eb
blessed.

Give Them All to Jesus

BOB BENSON, Sr. and P. J.

PHIL JOHNSON

CHORUS
Eb
Fm7/Bb
Eb
EbM9
down.
pain.
Give them all, give them all,
Fm7
Bb9sus
Bb9
Fm7
Bb9sus
give them all to Je - sus: Shat-tered dreams, wound-ed hearts, and bro - ken
Eb
Fm7/Bb
Eb
EbM9
toys. Give them all, give them all,
Fm7
Bb9sus
Bb9
Fm7
Bb9sus
Bb9
give them all to Je - sus; And He will turn your sor - row in - to
1
Eb
Bb13
2
Eb
joy!
joy!

Learning to Lean

J. S. JOHN STALLINGS

G G7 C D7/A
joy I can't ex - plain fills my soul Since the
glo - ri - ous vic - t'ry each day now for me,
G D/F♯ Em7 D7sus D7
day I made Je - sus my King. His
I found His peace so se - rene. He
G G7 C D7/A
bless - ed Ho - ly Spir - it is lead - ing my way; He's
helps me with each task if on - ly I'll ask; Ev - 'ry
G Em7 Am7 D7 G C/G G D7 D.S.
teach-ing, and I'm learn - ing to lean. I'm
day now I'm learn - ing to lean.
CODA
Am7 D7 G C/G G
Je - sus.

Mansion Builder

A. H.

ANNE HERRING

Ab Bb/Ab Eb/G Eb Ab Bb/Ab

Eb/G Eb 𝄋 Ab Bb/Ab Eb/G Eb

1. I've been told that there are those ___ who will
2. I've been told that there's a crys - tal ___ lake

Ab Bb/Ab Eb/G Eb Ab Bb/Ab

learn ___ how to fly; ___ And I've been told that ___
___ in the sky; ___ And ev - 'ry tear ___

Eb/G Eb Bb7

there are those ___ who will nev - er die. And
from my eyes ___ is ___ saved ___ when I cry. And

Ab Bb/Ab Eb/G Eb Ab Bb/Ab

I've been told that there are ___ stars that will nev - er lose their shine;
I've been told there'll come a ___ time when the sun will cease to shine;

Eb/G
Eb
Ab
Bb/Ab
Eb/G
Eb
And that there is a Morn - ing Star who
And that there is a Morn - ing Star who
Bb7
Eb/Bb
Slower
Ab
3
knows my mind.
knows my mind.
So why should I
Eb/G
Eb
Cm
Cm/Bb
F/A
F7
wor - ry? Why should I fret? 'Cause
Ab
Bb/Ab
Eb/G
Eb
Ab
F7/A
I've got a man - sion build - er who ain't through with me yet.
1,3
Bb9sus
Bb
Eb
2
Bb9sus
Bb7
D.S.
So
2. And

4
Bb9sus
Bb7
Eb
with me yet.
Eb/Db
F7/C
Abm/Cb
Abm6
Eb
rit.

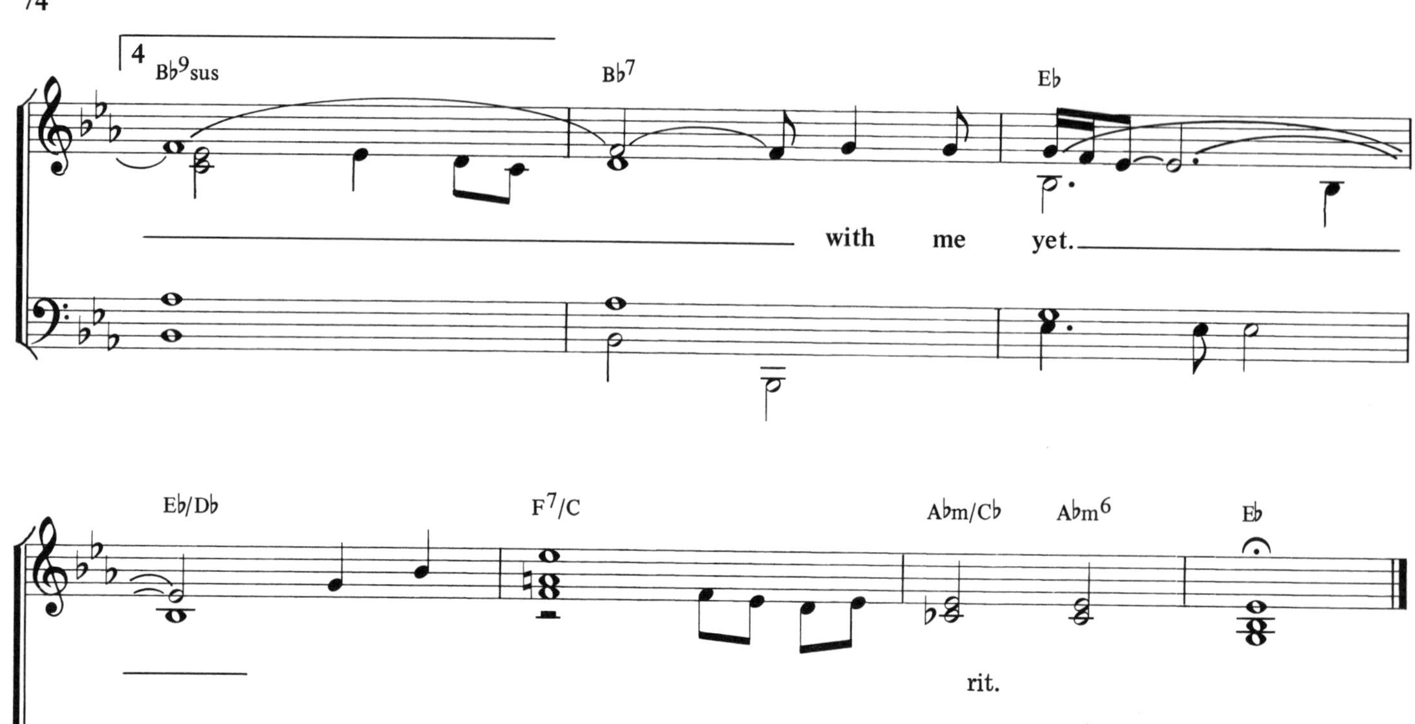

Pass It On

K. K.

KURT KAISER

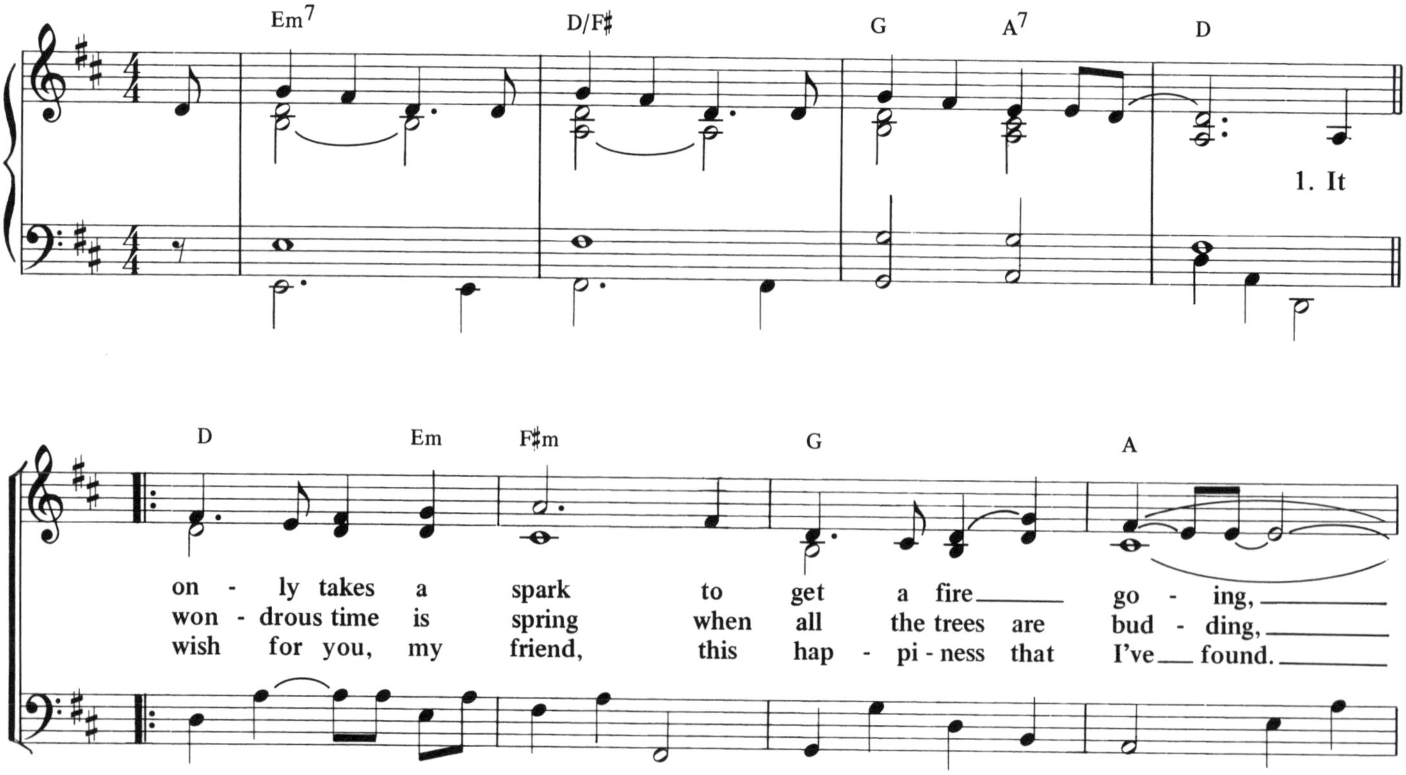
Em7
D/F#
G
A7
D
1. It
D
Em
F#m
G
A
on - ly takes a spark to get a fire go - ing,
won - drous time is spring when all the trees are bud - ding,
wish for you, my friend, this hap - pi - ness that I've found.

D Em F♯m G
And soon all those a - round can warm up in its
The birds be - gin to sing, the flow - ers start their
You can de - pend on Him; it mat - ters not where
A D G A/G D/F♯
glow - ing. That's how it is with God's love
bloom - ing. That's how it is with God's love
you're bound. I'll shout it from the moun - tain top,
Em F♯m G F♯m Bm Em7 D/F♯
once you've ex - per-i-enced it; You spread His love to ev - 'ry - one, you
once you've ex - per-i-enced it; You want to sing, it's fresh like spring, you
I want my world to know; The Lord of love has come to me, I
1,2 G A7 D 3 G A7
want to pass it on. 2. What a want to pass it
want to pass it on. 3. I
D G A7 D
on.

He Cares for Me

J. O.

JIMMY OWENS
Arr. by Ken Thomas

B♭
F
pow - er is great and will ev - er en - dure. His
Dm
Am
G9 G6
G7
C7sus C7
F7
wis - dom is peace - a - ble, gen - tle, and pure. But
B♭
F
Gm9
F/A
B♭
C7
great - er than all these glo - ries I see Is the
F
Am
F/A
Gm7
C7
1,2
F
B♭
glo - ri - ous prom - ise that He cares for me.
F
3
F
B♭
F/A
Gm7
F
2. The
3. He
me.

The New 23rd

R. C. RALPH CARMICHAEL

Am
p
C/G
F M7
E - ven when walk - ing thro' the dark val - ley___ of death, val - ley of
Em
Am/C
mf
E/B
Am
D/F♯
death,___ I will nev - er be a - fraid; For
G
F/G
mp
G
C
F/C
He___ is close be - side___ me, guard-ing, guid-ing all the way. He
G/B
C
F
C/E
spreads a feast be - fore___ me in the pres - ence of my
F
G/F
C/E
G/D
C
en - e - mies. He___ wel - comes me as His spe - cial guest. With

C7/B♭
A
D/F♯
Dm/F
bless - ing o - ver - flow - ing, His good - ness and un - fail - ing
E
E/D
Am/C
E/B
Am
kind - ness shall be with me all of my life; And
D/F♯
Dm/F
G/F
C/E
Dm7
C
C/B♭
A♭
af - ter - ward I will live with Him for - ev - er, for -
G sus
C
F/C
ev - er in His home; For - ev - er in His
C
F/C
C
home, for - ev - er in His home.

Sweet, Sweet Spirit

D. A. DORIS AKERS

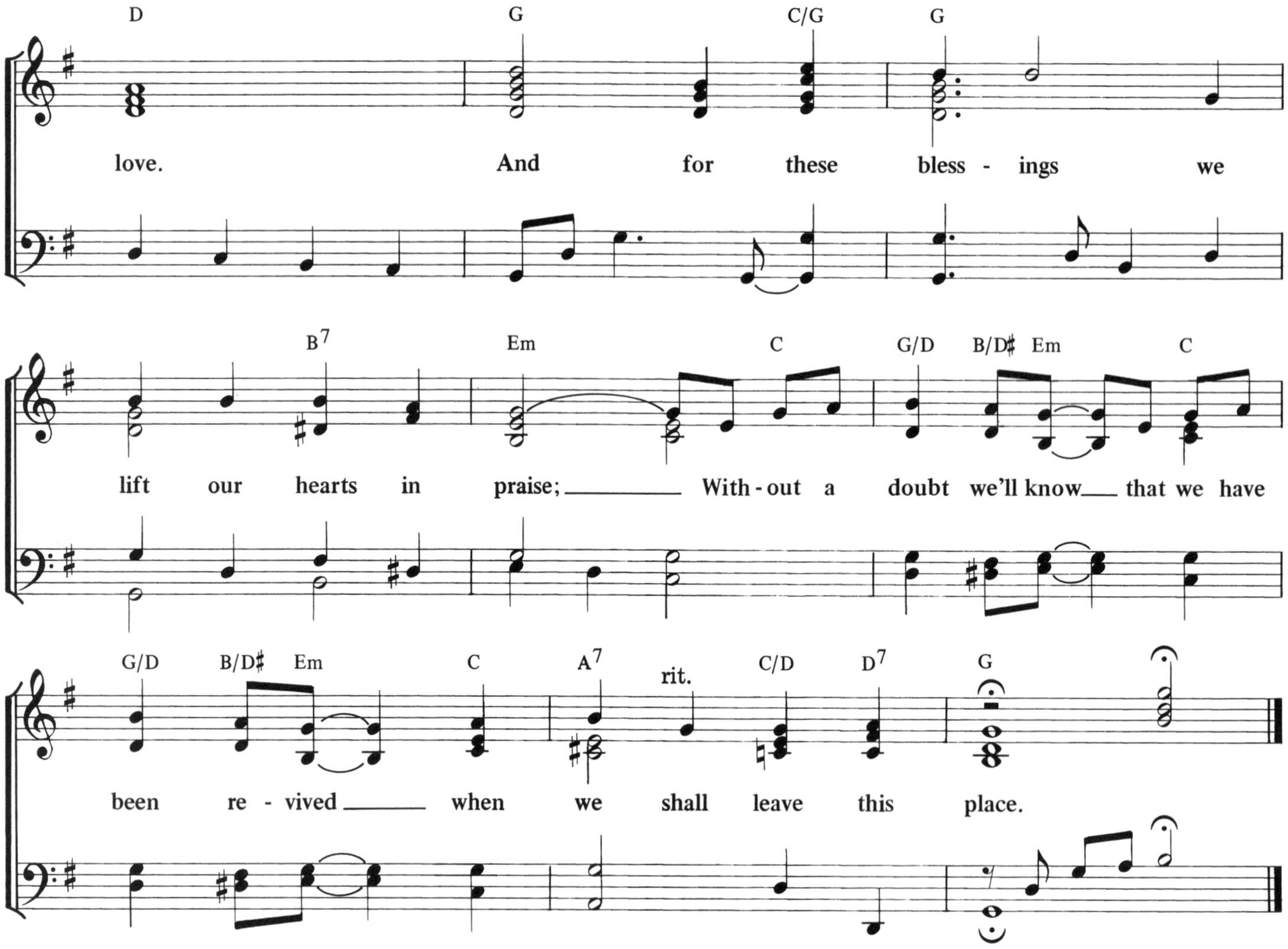
D G C/G G
love. And for these bless - ings we
B7 Em C G/D B/D♯ Em C
lift our hearts in praise; With - out a doubt we'll know that we have
G/D B/D♯ Em C A7 rit. C/D D7 G
been re - vived when we shall leave this place.

The Bond of Love

O. S.

OTIS SKILLINGS
Arr. by Ken Thomas

B♭ B♭+
1. Love through Christ has
2. Now, dear Lord, we
E♭/B♭ B♭ F7
brought us to - geth - er, Melt - ing our hearts as one.
join in wor - ship; Thank You for all You've done.

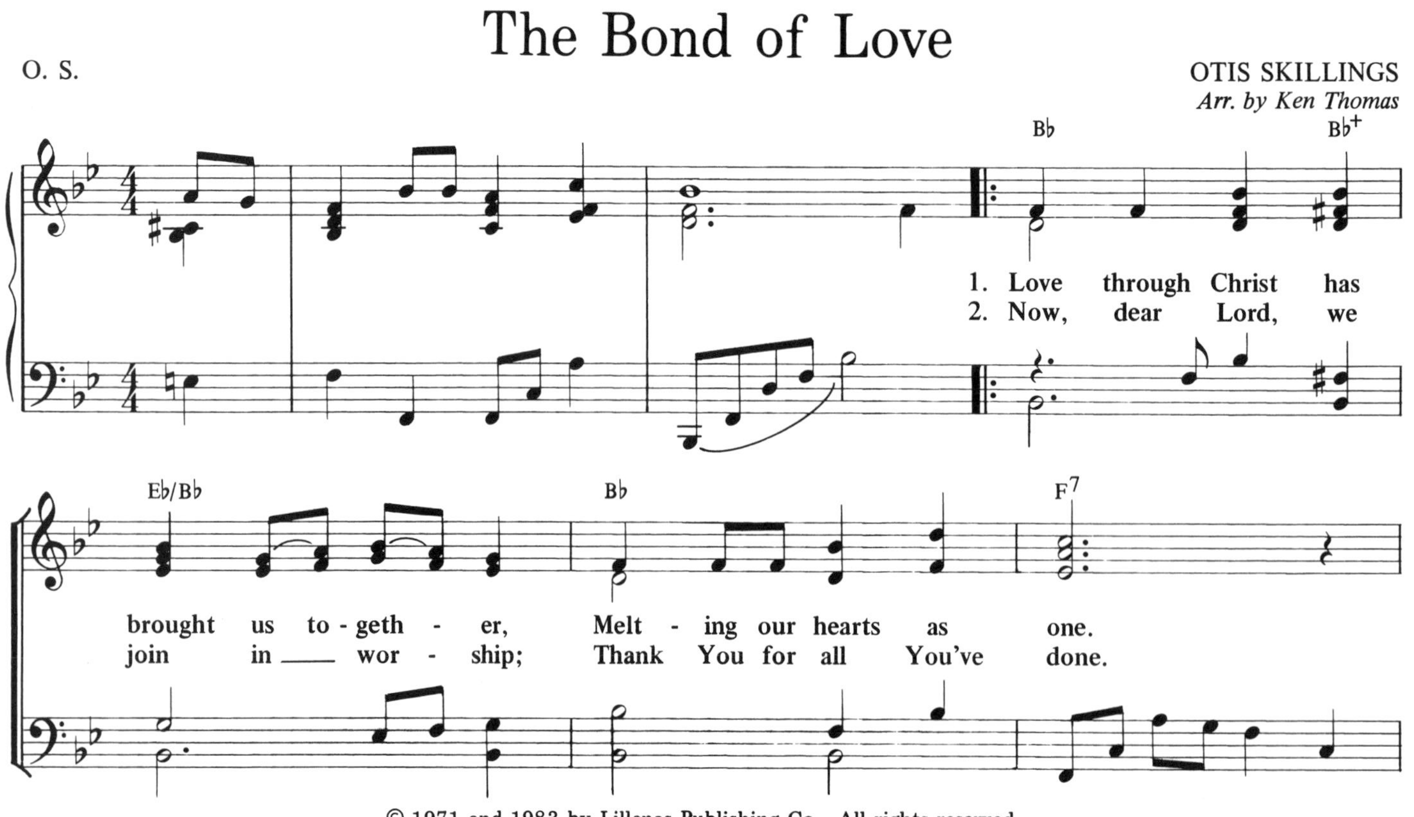

Bb Bb/D Eb Bb/F F7
By God's Spir - it we are u - nit - ed, One through His bless - ed
Thank You for this love You gave us; Thank You for mak - ing us
Bb Bb Eb/Bb Bb
Son. We are one in the bond of love. We are
one. Let us sing now, ev - 'ry - one; Let us
Gm C7/E Cm7 F7 Bb F7 Bb7
one in the bond of love. We have joined our spir - it with the
feel His love be - gun. Let us join our hands so the
Eb E° Bb/F F7 1 Bb
Spir - it of God; We are one in the bond of love.
world will know We are one in the bond of
2 Bb E° Bb/F F7 Bb
love. We are one in the bond of love.
rit.

Gentle Shepherd

GLORIA GAITHER and W. J. G.

WILLIAM J. GAITHER

F
Am
F7
There's no oth - er we can
Bb
G9
turn to Who can help us
Gm7
C7
F
face an - oth - er day. Gen - tle Shep - herd,
G9/F
Gm
come and lead us, For we need
C
F
Bb
F
rit.
You to help us find our way.

Statue of Liberty

N. E.

NEIL ENLOE

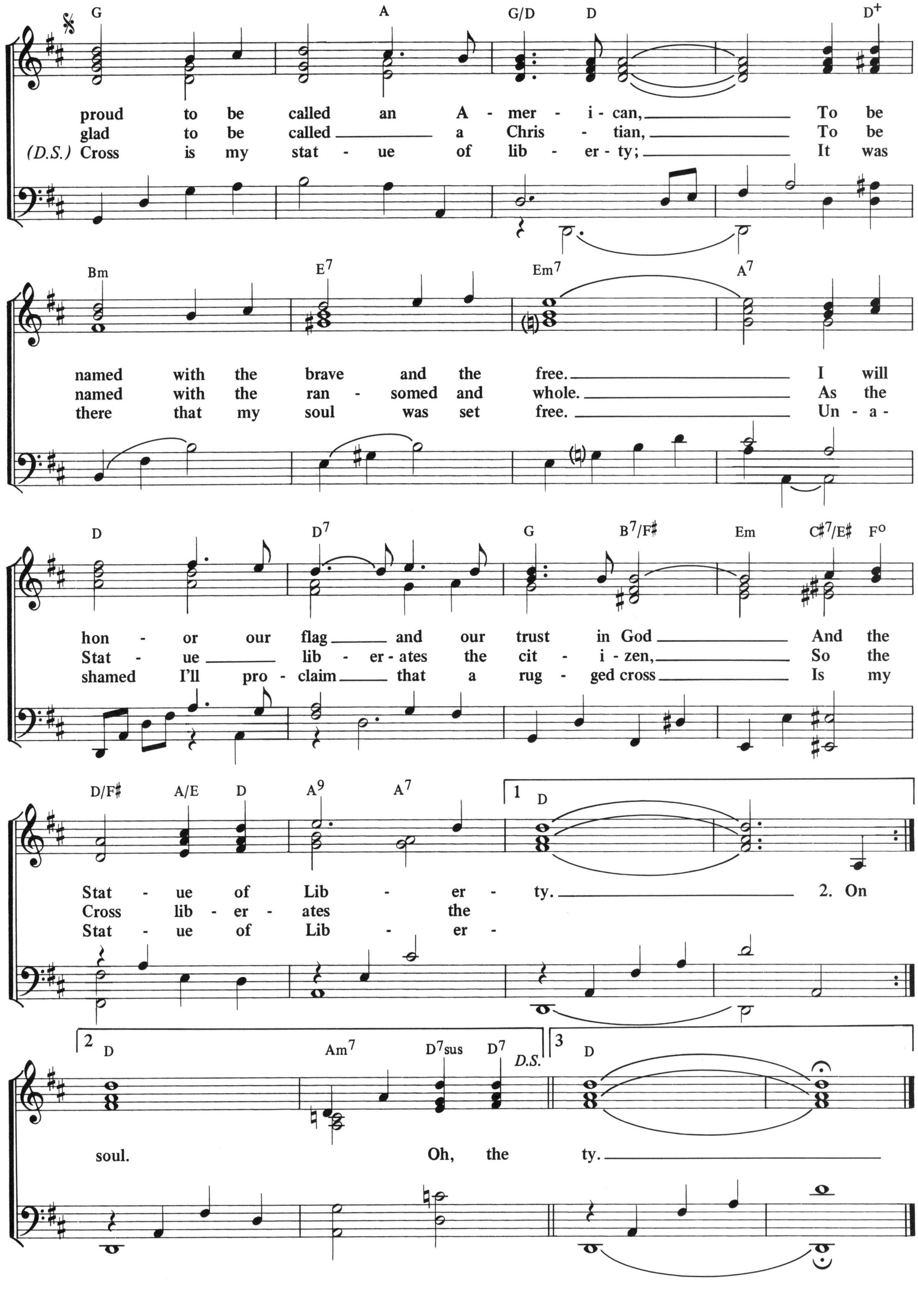

G A G/D D D+

proud to be called an A - mer - i - can, To be
glad to be called a Chris - tian, To be
(D.S.) Cross is my stat - ue of lib - er - ty; It was

Bm E7 Em7 A7

named with the brave and the free. I will
named with the ran - somed and whole. As the
there that my soul was set free. Un - a -

D D7 G B7/F♯ Em C♯7/E♯ F°

hon - or our flag and our trust in God And the
Stat - ue lib - er - ates the cit - i - zen, So the
shamed I'll pro - claim that a rug - ged cross Is my

D/F♯ A/E D A9 A7 1 D

Stat - ue of Lib - er - ty. 2. On
Cross lib - er - ates the
Stat - ue of Lib - er -

2 D Am7 D7sus D7 D.S. 3 D

soul. Oh, the ty.

The Trees of the Field

STEFFI GEISER RUBIN

STUART DAUERMANN
Arr. by Ken Thomas

Em D7 G C/G G
hands; And all the trees of the field will
D D7
clap their hands. The trees of the fields will
G C/G G
clap their hands. The trees of the field will
D G D7 Em B7
clap their hands while you go out with
Em
joy. You shall go
D.S. al Coda
CODA
Em
hands.
8va

I Want Jesus More than Anything

D. M. DON MARSH

CHORUS
C F/C G F/G G7
thing.
paid.
Take the fame that I might want and all the
F/C C Em/G Dm/G G7
things that seem so dear; I'd rath - er have Him than an - y praise that men may
F/C C F/C G F/G G7
give to me. I want Him to have con - trol and be the
F/C C Em/G Dm/G Em/G G7
breath of life in me; I'd rath - er have Je - sus, I'd rath-er have Him than an - y -
1 C F/G G7
thing.
2. He had
2 C Dm/C C7 B♭/D C7/E
thing.
As I go

on through life with Him, there can be no oth - er way; I want
Je - sus more than an - y - thing.
rit.
H. L.
My Wonderful Lord
HALDOR LILLENAS
Arr. by Ken Thomas
1. I have found a deep peace that I nev - er had known, And a
(2. I de -) sire that my life shall be or - dered by Thee, That my
(3. All the) tal - ents I have I have laid at Thy feet; Thy ap-
(4. Thou art) fair - er to me than the fair - est on earth, Thou om-

D/F♯ A7/E D G G7
joy this world could not af - ford Since I yield - ed con - trol of my
will be in per - fect ac - cord With Thine own sov-'reign will, Thy de-
prov - al shall be my re - ward. Be my store great or small, I sur-
ni - po - tent, life - giv - ing Word. O Thou An - cient of Days, Thou art
C G/D D9 D7 G C/G G
REFRAIN
bod - y and soul To my won - der - ful, won - der - ful Lord.
sires to ful - fill, My won - der - ful, won - der - ful Lord. My
ren - der it all To my won - der - ful, won - der - ful Lord.
wor - thy all praise, My won - der - ful, won - der - ful Lord.
G C G
won - der - ful Lord, my won - der - ful Lord, By an - gels and ser - aphs in
D G G7 C
heav - en a - dored! I bow at Thy shrine, my Sav - ior di - vine, My
G/D D7 1-3 G C/G G 4 G C/G G
won-der-ful, won - der-ful Lord.
2. I de-
3. All the
4. Thou art
Lord.

The Easter Song

A. H. ANNE HERRING

Dm
Dm7/C
B♭M7
Am
Quick - ly now, go tell His dis - ci - ples that Je - sus
CM7/G
F
C/E
Christ is no long - er dead!" Joy to the
Dm
Dm/C
B♭
F
B♭
F
world, He is ris - en, al - le - lu - ia! He's
C
G
C
G
C
F
C
ris - en, al - le - lu - ia! He's ris - en, al -
F
le - lu - ia!

Sometimes Alleluia

C. G.

CHUCK GIRARD

F/C C F G7 F/C C Am
sing. O let us now re - turn His love;
air. O let us sing of Je - sus' love
Dm7 1 C/G G7 2 C/G G G/A A7
just let our voic - es ring!
to peo - ple ev - 'ry - where!
D G A7
Some-times "al - le - lu - ia," some-times "praise the
D G/A D B Em
Lord!" Some-times gent - ly sing - ing,
A7 D sus D A7 D sus D
our hearts in one ac - cord.

Bread upon the Water

B. G. and J. G.

BILL & JANNY GREIN

Db Eb Ab Db/Eb Ab
come back home on ev - 'ry wave. You got to keep on cast - in' your bread up-on the
Bb7 Db Eb Ab
wa - ter; Soon it's gon-na come back home on ev - 'ry wave. Good mea-sure, pressed down,
Bb7
2nd time to Coda
Db Eb7
shak-en to-geth - er, run-ning o - ver; Soon it's gon-na come back home on ev - 'ry
Ab
D.S. al Coda
CODA
Db Eb
wave.
come back home on ev - 'ry
Ab Bb7/Ab Db/Ab Bbm7/Eb Ab
wave.

I've Got Confidence

A. C.

ANDRAÉ CROUCH

G7 C7 F7 B♭
I've got con - fi - dence; God is gon - na see me through.
G7 C7 F7
No mat - ter what the case may be I know He's gon - na
B♭ G7 C7 F7
fix it for me. I've got con - fi - dence; God
B♭ G7 C7
is gon - na see me through. No mat - ter what the case may be,
F7 B♭ F7 B♭
I know He's gon - na fix it for me.

If That Isn't Love

D. R.

DOTTIE RAMBO

B♭ E♭/B♭ B♭ F

dry, ___ There's no star in the sky, And the

F7 B♭ Fm7 B♭13 B♭9/D E♭

spar - row ___ can't fly! ___ If that is - n't love, ___

A♭/E♭ E♭ B♭ E♭/B♭ B♭

___ Then heav - en's a myth; ___ There's no feel - ing like

F Cm7 F F7 1 B♭ F9sus

this, If that is - n't love.

2 B♭ E♭/B♭ E♭m6/B♭ B♭

love. ___

All of Me
M. L.
MOSIE LISTER
Arr. by Ken Thomas
simile
1. All of me, not a part but all of me;
2. Use me, Lord; use me an - y where at all.
All the heart and soul of me, Je - sus, I sur - ren - der.
Though my place be great or small, Let me fill it glad - ly.
I be-lieve; Lord, help my un - be - lief!
Take my life; be it poor or be it grand,
On the al - tar now I lay all I am to - day.
Let me live it by Your plan; shape it with Your hand.

REFRAIN
B♭ Cm7 F7 B♭
As I am I come to Thee with - out one plea;
E♭/B♭ B♭ G7 C/G G7 C sus
On - ly that Thy sav - ing blood was shed for me.
C F Am7 Gm7 C7 F Am
All of me through the a - ges yet to be,
Gm7 C7 F Dm Gm7 C/E Dm Gm7 C7
I sur - ren - der, Lord, to Thee; I sur - ren - der all of
1 F
me.
2 Dm Dm/C Gm7 C7sus C7 F
me.
rit.

Holy Spirit, Thou Art Welcome

DOTTIE RAMBO

DOTTIE RAMBO and DAVE HUNTSINGER

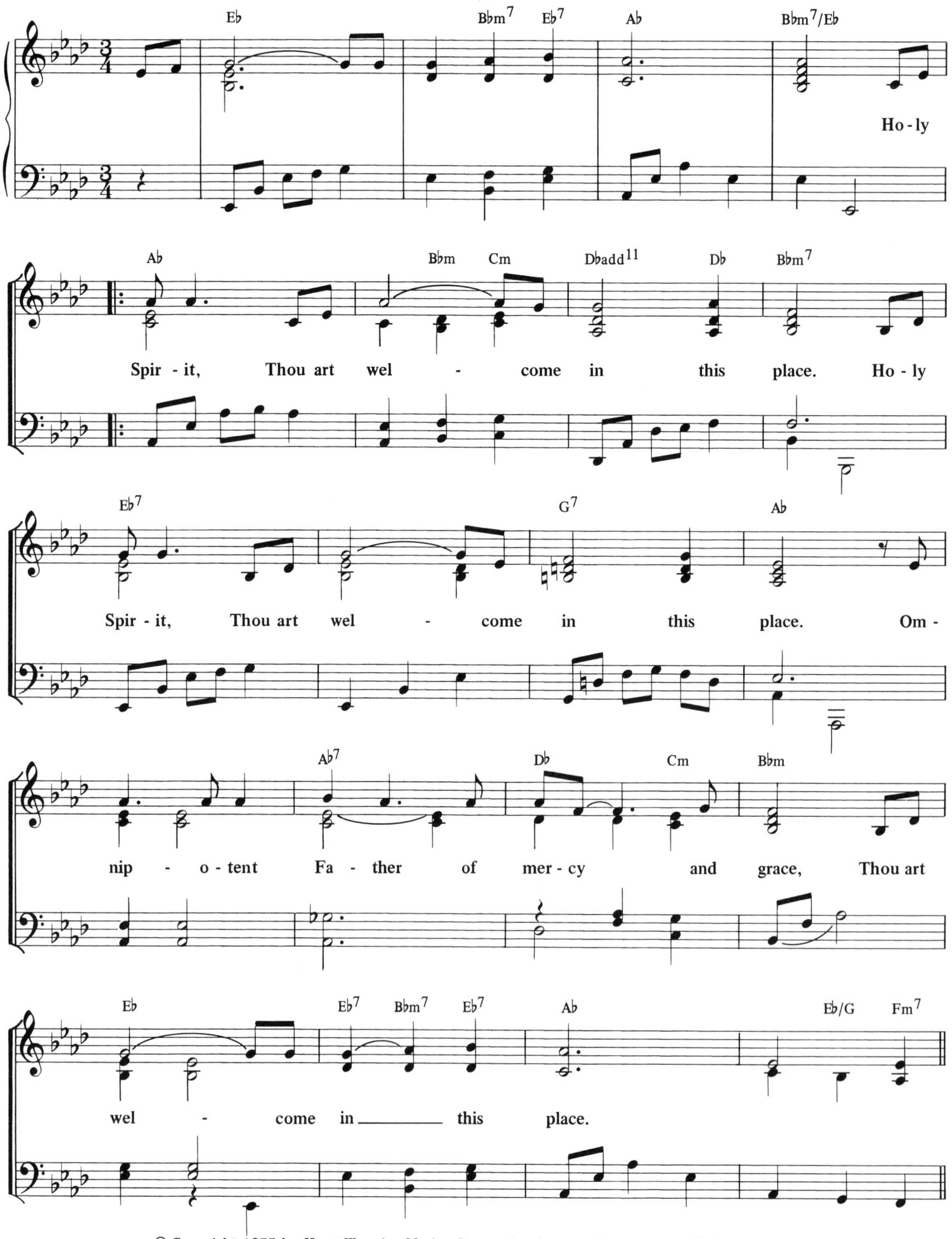

Ho - ly
Spir - it, Thou art wel - come in this place. Ho - ly
Spir - it, Thou art wel - come in this place. Om -
nip - o - tent Fa - ther of mer - cy and grace, Thou art
wel - come in ______ this place.

Eb7 Bbm7 Eb7 Db Cm7 Bbm7 Ab
1. Lord, in Thy pres - ence there's heal - ing di - vine;
2. Fill all the hun - gry and emp - ty with - in; Re -
Db Ab Bb7 Bbm7
No oth - er pow - er can save, Lord, but Thine.
store us, O Fa - ther, re - vive us a - gain.
Eb7 Ab Bbm Cm Dbadd11
Ho - ly Spir - it, Thou art wel - come in this
Ho - ly Spir - it, Thou art wel - come in this
Bbm7 Eb7 Bbm7 Eb7 1 Ab Bbm7/Eb
place; Thou art wel - come in this place. Ho - ly
place; Thou art wel - come in this
2 Ab Db/Ab Eb7 Ab
place.

Is It Any Wonder?

CAROL and JIMMY OWENS

JIMMY OWENS
Arr. by Ken Thomas

Am7 D7 Am7 D7 G GM9 G♯o

cried to Him and prayed; Then He saved my soul and that is why I say:
hap-pi-ness a-gain, Then I want the world to hear me when I say:
Tell me,

Am7 D7 GM7 Am7 D7

is it __ an-y won-der __ that I love Him __ when you con-sid-er all He's done for

simile

GM7 G7 Dm7 G7 C

me? And is it an-y won-der that I want to do His will, And

A9 Am7/D D7 Am7 D7

let His light shine out for all to see? And is it __ an-y won-der __ that I

GM7 Am7 D7 GM7 G7

praise Him __ Each time I __ think of how He's made me free? And

Dm7 G7 C Am7 1 G/D Em7 Am7 C/D D7
is it an - y won - der that I've giv - en Him my heart When Je - sus free - ly gave His life for
G Am7 D7 2 G/D Em7 Am7 C/D D7 G
me? 2. When I Je - sus free - ly gave His life for me?

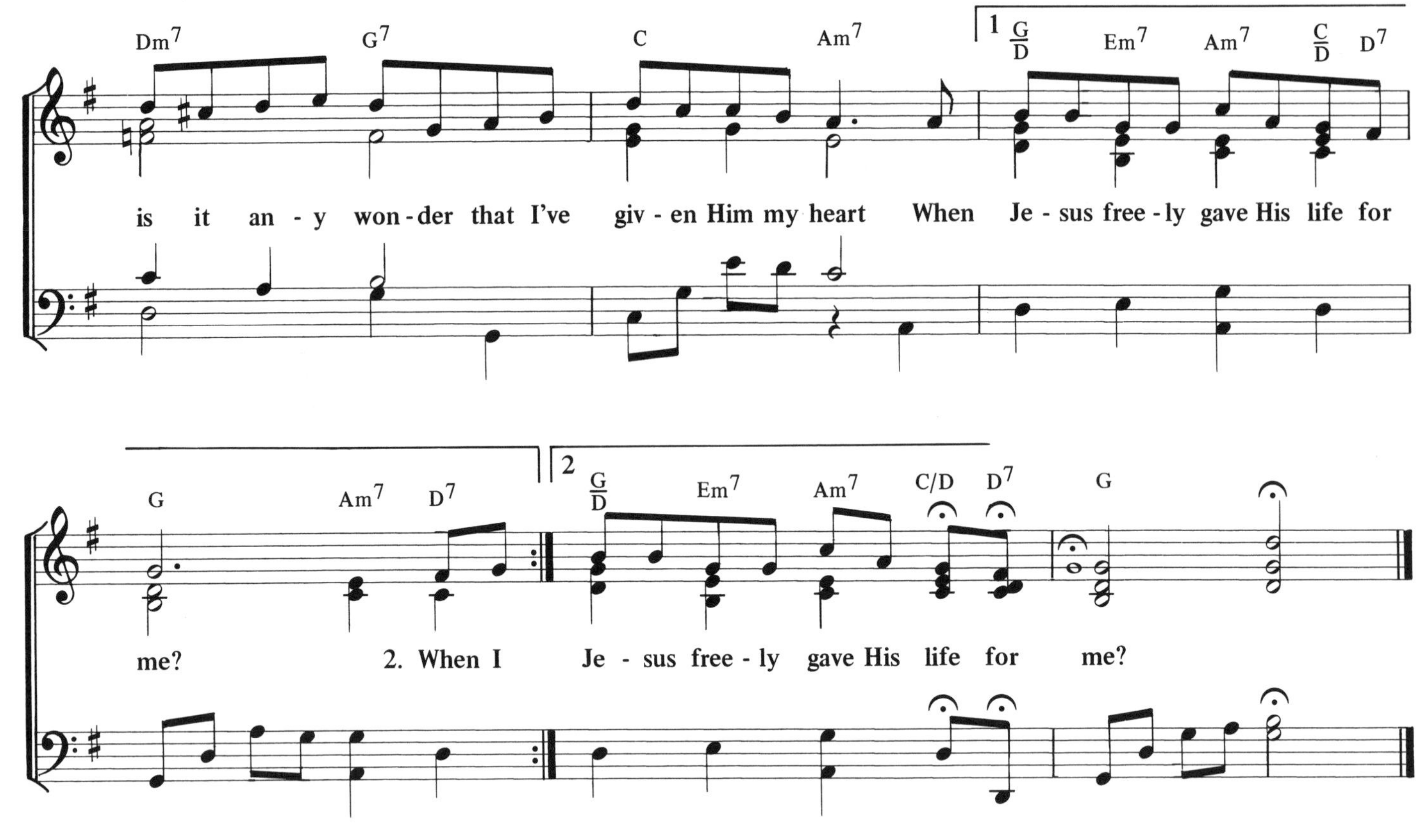

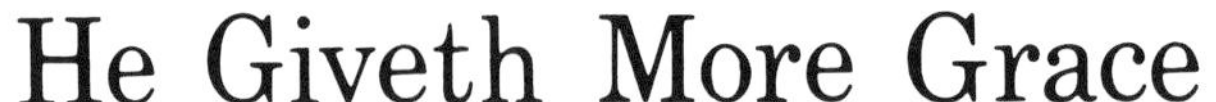

He Giveth More Grace

ANNE JOHNSON FLINT

HUBERT MITCHELL
Arr. by Ken Thomas

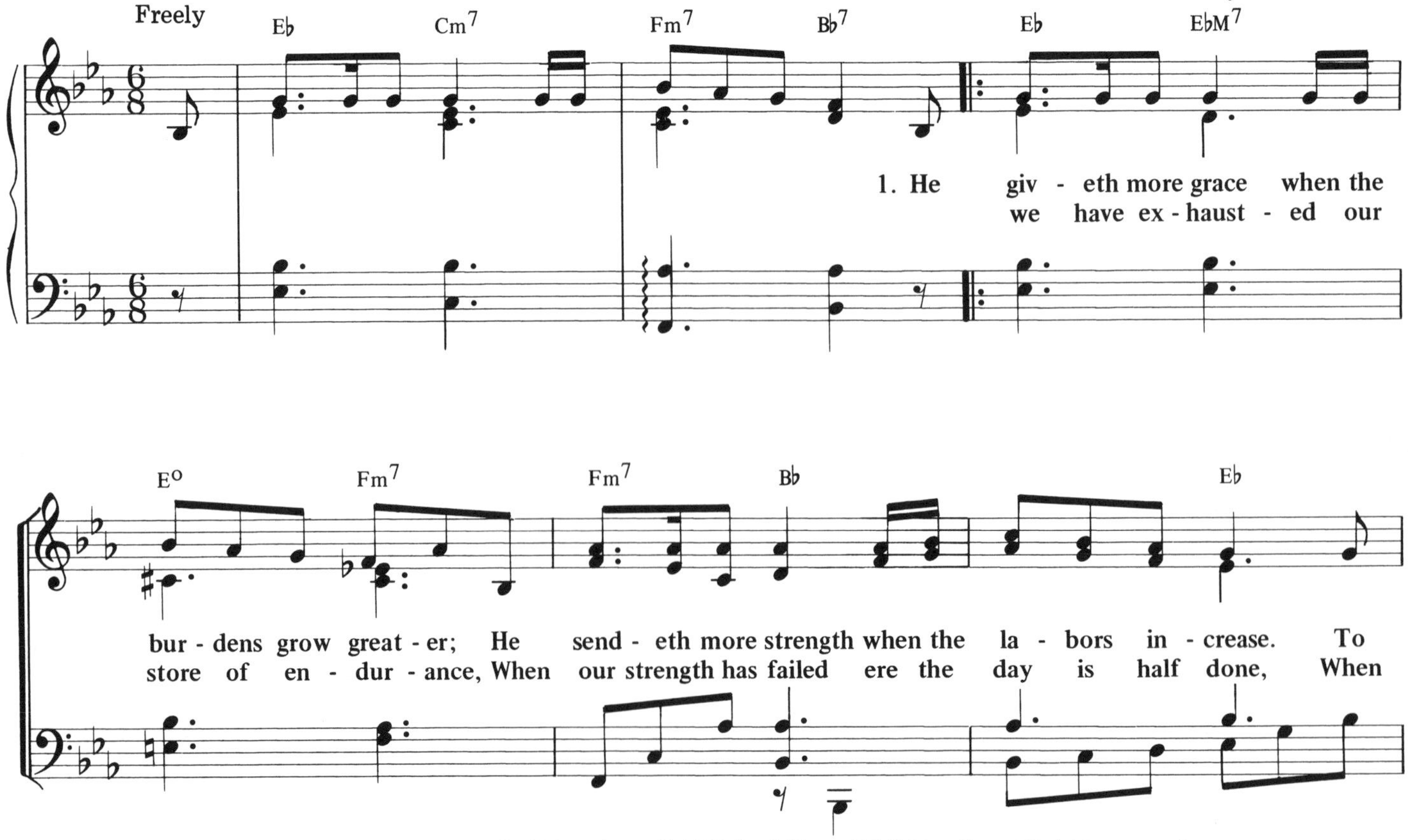
Freely
Eb Cm7 Fm7 Bb7 Eb EbM7
1. He giv - eth more grace when the
we have ex - haust - ed our
E° Fm7 Fm7 Bb Eb
bur - dens grow great - er; He send - eth more strength when the la - bors in - crease. To
store of en - dur - ance, When our strength has failed ere the day is half done, When

add - ed af - flic - tion He add - eth His mer - cy; To mul - ti - plied tri - als, His
we reach the end of our hoard - ed re - sourc - es, Our Fa - ther's full giv - ing is
REFRAIN
mul - ti - plied peace.
on - ly be - gun.
His love has no lim - it; His grace has no meas - ure; His
pow'r has no boun - da - ry known un - to men. For out of His in - fi - nite
rich - es in Je - sus, He giv - eth and giv - eth, and giv - eth a - gain. 2. When
giv - eth a - gain.
rit.

Learning to Live Like a Child of the King

WILLIAM J. and GLORIA GAITHER
and GARY S. PAXTON

WILLIAM J. GAITHER and GARY S. PAXTON

D/A Am7 D9 G
Learn-ing to mas - ter by the way that I serve; Be - ing de - pen - dent on His
G♯o D/A Bm7 E7 A7
bless-ing re - serve, I gave Him my soul. He's got to - tal con - trol!
D D6 DM7
Learn-ing to live like a child of the King, Learn-ing to lose just to
D B7 Em Em/A A7
find ev - 'ry - thing; Ac - cept-ing His wealth tho' I had noth-ing to bring,
Em A7 Em/D D A7/D D
Learn-ing to live free and hap - py.

Then I Met the Master
M. L.
MOSIE LISTER
Arr. by Ken Thomas
Dm7/G G13 G7 C
1. Like a
C C6 G7 G
babe when it cries for its moth - er, Like a child I was
blind man who walks in the dark - ness, I had longed, I had
G7 C F
help - less, a - lone. Then I met the
searched for the light. Then I met the
C C/G G9 Em/G G7 C
Mas - ter; Now I am one of His own.
Mas - ter; Now I walk no more in the night.
REFRAIN
G7 Dm7 G7 F/G F/C C
For all things were changed when He found me; A

G7 Dm7 G7 F/G F/C C F
new day broke through all a - round me. For I
C C/G G9
met the Mas - ter; Now I be -
1 G13 G7 C G13
long to Him. 2. Like a
2 G13 G+
long to Him.
F6 F Fm6 C A7/E
I met the Mas - ter; Now
Dm Dm7 Em/G G7 C F/C F/G C
I be - long to Him.

Something Beautiful

GLORIA GAITHER | WILLIAM J. GAITHER

Eb Fm7 Bb7 Eb Ebo Eb Bb7 Bbo

Some - thing beau-ti - ful, some - thing

Bb7 Fm Fm7# Fm7 Bb7 Eb

good; All my con - fu - sion He un - der -

Bbm7 Eb7 Ab Ab/Eb Eb G7/D

stood. All I had to of - fer Him was bro - ken - ness and

Cm Cm/Bb Ab6 Eb/Bb Bb7 *2nd time to Coda*

strife, But He made some - thing beau-ti-ful of my

Eb Ab/Eb Eb Rubato Eb EbM7 Eb6 F#o

life. If there ev - er were dreams that were loft - y and no - ble,

Fm7 Bb7 Fm7 Fm7#
They were my dreams at the start; And the hopes for life's best were the
Fm7 Bb7 Ab/Eb Eb Eb° Eb
hopes that I har - bored down deep in my heart. But my
Eb EbM7 Bbm7 Eb7 Absus Ab
dreams turned to ash - es, my cas - tles all crum-bled, My for - tune turned to
Begin slow rhythm
Ab6 Cm F7 Cm7 F7 Fm7/Bb Bb6 Fm/Bb Eb/Bb
loss; So I wrapped it all in the rags of my life And laid it at the
Bb9
D.S. al Coda
CODA
Eb Ab Ab/Bb Eb
Cross! life!

If My People Will Pray

2 Chronicles 7:14
Adapted by J. O.

JIMMY OWENS

C sus
F
E♭
F/E♭
B♭/D
ways; Then will I hear from heav - en;
Cm
F
B♭sus
B♭
Gm
C9/E
then will I hear from heav - en. Then will I hear and will for -
mp
mf
F sus
F
E♭/F
F
B♭
F/A
give, for - give their sin. If My peo - ple
rit.
mp
a tempo
A♭
E♭/G
E♭m/G♭
B♭sus/F
B♭/F
which are called by My name shall hum - ble them-selves, shall hum - ble them-
C9/E
E♭
selves and pray, I will for - give their sin,
mf
cresc. poco a poco

Bb/D
Eb/Db
I will for - give their sin, I will for - give their sin
Cm7
F sus
F7
Bb
ff
mp
and heal their land. If My
F/A
Ab
Eb/G
Ebm/Gb
peo - ple which are called by My name shall hum - ble them-selves, shall
Bbsus/F
Bb/F
Cm7
F7sus
hum - ble them-selves, shall hum - ble them-selves and
Bb
F/A
Fm/Ab
Eb/G
F sus
Bb
pray.
rit.

The Day of Miracles

M. L.

MOSIE LISTER
Arr. by Ken Thomas

G7 F/G C Am Dm
Some folks say that mir - a - cles are not for to -
G7 C Am Em Dm/F Dm
day; They say that it's old - fash - ioned to trust and to
G G7 C C+ Am Dm
mf
pray. But I be - lieve that mir - a - cles still hap - pen to -
Fm6/D C/G Am D9 G
day For those who pray and be - lieve.
C Am Dm
If you say to that moun - tain, "Be cast in the

G7 C Am Em Dm
sea," Have faith that nev - er fal - ters and so shall it
G7 C+ Am Am/G
mf
be. The One who moves that moun - tain still cares for you and
D/F# C/G E/G# Am 1 Dm7 G7
f
me; And the day of mir - a - cles is the day you be -
C Em Am Dm7 G13
lieve.
2 Dm7 G7 Dm7/G G7 C
day you be - lieve.

Redemption Draweth Nigh

G. J.

GORDON JENSEN

CHORUS
B♭
F
F/C
C♯o
Signs of the times are ev - 'ry - where,
And there's a
Dm
F7/C
B♭
F
C7
brand - new feel - ing in the air.
Keep your
F
C7/G
F/A
B♭
A7
eyes up - on the east - ern sky,
Lift up your
Dm
B♭
F/C
C
C7
1
F
head, re - demp - tion draw - eth nigh.
2. Wars and
2
F
D♭/F
E♭/F
F
nigh.
R.H.

Part the Waters

C. F. B.

CHARLES F. BROWN

FM7/G FM7 Em7 Dm7 Dm7/G F/C Em/C Dm/C Em/C
1. Know-ing You love me through the bur - dens I must bear; Hear-ing Your
2. Know-ing You love me helps me face an-oth - er day; Hear-ing Your
Dm7 Dm7/G Dm7/C C Bm7 E7 Am Em/G
foot-steps lets me know I'm in Your care; And in the night of my life You
foot-steps drives the clouds and fears a - way; And in the tears of my life I
FM7 G7/F C/E D7sus D7 G7sus G7
bring the prom-ise of day. Here is my hand; show me the way. When I
see the sor - row You bore. Here is my pain; heal it once more.
CODA
C/G G7sus E/G♯ Am E/G♯
life, still the rag - ing storm in me. Touch my
C/G Dm7/G G7 N.C. F F/G C
life, still the rag - ing storm in me.

How Long Has It Been?

M. L.

MOSIE LISTER
Arr. by Ken Thomas

1. How

long has it been since you talked with the Lord And
long has it been since you knelt by your bed And

told Him your heart's hid - den se - crets? How
prayed to the Lord up in heav - en? How

long since you prayed? How long since you stayed On your
long since you knew that He'd an - swer you And would

knees 'til the light shone through? How
keep you the long night through? How

G C#o/G G C#o/G G B7
long has it been since your mind felt at ease? How
long has it been since you woke with the dawn And
C Co C D7 C/G G
long since your heart knew no bur - den? Can you
felt that the day's worth the liv - ing?
C B B7 Em A7
call Him your friend? How long has it been Since you
G/D D13 D7 1 G C/G G D7
knew that He cared for you? 2. How
2 G C/G Cm/G G
you?

Something Worth Living For

F C13 C7 F Gm7/C F
some-thing worth liv - ing for."
some-thing worth liv - ing for. Some - thing
some-thing worth liv - ing for.
C13 C7 F B♭ F/A G9
more than my yes - ter - days, More than I had be -
C G7 C F F7
fore, Some - thing more than
B♭/D F/C B♭ B° F/C C13 C7
wealth or fame; He gave me some-thing worth liv - ing
1 F Gm7/C
for.
2 F B♭/F F
for.

Communion Song

B. McG.

BARRY McGUIRE

B♭
E♭
B♭
Take it, eat it;
Take it, drink it;
Cm7
F
E♭
F13
Each time you do, re - mem - ber
B♭
E♭
F13
B♭
Me, re - mem - ber Me.
CODA
B♭
E♭M7
F6
B♭
E♭
F
Me. Re-mem-ber Me, re-mem-ber
B♭
rit.
E♭M7
F6
B♭
Me, re-mem-ber Me.
8va

Come, Holy Spirit

Wm. J. and GLORIA GAITHER — WILLIAM J. GAITHER

REFRAIN
G C/G G D6 D7
Come, Ho - ly Spir - it, I need Thee;
Am7 D7 G
Come, sweet Spir - it, I pray.
G7 F/G G7/F C/E Cm/E♭
Come, in Thy strength and Thy pow - er;
G/D D7
Come, in Thine own gen - tle
1,2
G C/G
way.
3
G C/G D G/D D7 G
way.

For Those Tears I Died

M. J. S. MARSHA J. STEVENS

REFRAIN
Eb Ab Eb
Je - sus said, "Come to the wa - ter, stand by My side. I
Bb Eb/Bb Bb7 Eb
know you are thir - sty; you won't be de - nied. I
Eb7 Db/Eb Eb7 Ab Eb
felt ev - 'ry tear - drop when in dark - ness you cried;
Bb Bb7 Cm7 Bb7/D
And I strove to re - mind you that for those tears I
1,2 3
Eb Eb Ab/Eb Bb9sus Eb
died. 2. Your died.
3.

Clean Before My Lord

HONEYTREE HONEYTREE

G
G6
GM7
G6
CM7
1. Why did I
me.
2. Oh, why do you
C6
Em
wait so long
wait so long
To
To
Am7
C/D
GM7
G6
learn such a liv - ing song?
learn such a liv - ing song?
GM7
G6
CM7
C6
And how could I stay so
And how can you stay so
Em
Am
Bm7
close With-out see - ing Him,
close With-out see - ing Him,

C
CM7
D
D7sus
D.S. twice
never seeing Him?
never seeing Him?
CODA
G
G6
GM7
G6
G
me.
Holy, Holy
J. O.
JIMMY OWENS
Dm
G7
Csus
C
G7
C
Dm7
G7
1. Ho-ly, ho-ly, ho-ly, ho-ly, Ho-ly,
Fa-ther, gra-cious Fa-ther, We're so
Dm7
G7
F/C
C
C7
F
Dm
D♯o
C/E
Em
ho-ly Lord God Al-might-y; And we lift our hearts be-fore You as a to-ken of our
blest to be Your chil-dren, gra-cious Fa-ther; And we lift our heads be-fore You as a to-ken of our
Am
Dm7
G
G7
1
F/C
C
F/G
2
F/C
C
A♭7
love; Ho-ly, ho-ly, ho-ly. ho-ly. 2. Gra-cious
love; Gra-cious Fa-ther, gra-cious Fa-ther. 3. Pre-cious

D♭ E♭m7 A♭7 E♭m7 A♭7 G♭/D♭ D♭ D♭7
Je - sus, pre-cious Je - sus, We're so glad that You've re-deemed us, pre-cious Je - sus; And we
G♭ E♭m E° D♭/F Fm B♭m E♭m7 A♭7 G♭/D♭ D♭ A7
lift our hands before You as a to-ken of our love, Pre-cious Je - sus, pre-cious Je - sus. 4. Ho - ly
D Em7 A7 Em7 A7 G/D D D7
Spir - it, Ho - ly Spir - it, Come and fill our hearts a - new, Ho - ly Spir - it; And we
G Em F° D/F♯ F♯m Bm Em A7
lift our voice be-fore You as a to - ken of our love, Ho - ly Spir - it, Ho - ly
G/D D Em A7 G/D D
Spir - it.

'Til the Storm Passes By

M. L.

MOSIE LISTER
Arr. by Ken Thomas

D/A
A7
D
safe 'til the storm pass - es by.
storms nev - er dark - en the skies. 'Til the
Thee when the storm pass - es by.
REFRAIN
A
A7
D
3
E7
storm pass-es o - ver, 'til the thun-der sounds no more, 'Til the clouds roll for-
A
A7
D
D7
ev - er from the sky, Hold me fast; let me stand in the
G
D/F♯
Em7
D/F♯
G
D/A
A7
hol - low of Thy hand. Keep me safe 'til the storm pass - es
1,2
D
G/A
3
D
by.
2. Man - y
3. When the
by.

Tree Song

K. M. KEN MEDEMA

D
G/D
Em
A7
This is the song that my tree friend sang to me: "I've got
G
A
roots grow-ing down to the wa - ter; I've got leaves grow-ing up to the sun - shine; And the
shade from the hot sum-mer sun-down; I am nest for the birds of the heav - en. I'm be -
fruit that I bear is a sign of the life in me. I am
com-ing what the Lord of
1,3,5
Bm7
2,4
Bm
Em7
A sus
trees has meant me to be: a strong young tree."
D.S.
6
trees has meant me to be: a strong young tree."

Unworthy

D. B. THOMAS

GLORIA ROE

Gm7
C7
F
F♯o
Gm7
I am un - wor - thy of the place He has pre -
C7
Gm
G♯o
Am
pared. I am un - wor - thy of His love that He has
C7
Dm
F/C
B♭
D7
Gm
E7/G♯
shared. I am un - wor - thy to claim His pre-cious name; Yet He
Am
D7
Gm
C7
F
B♭/F
F
E7/G♯
loved me, still He loves me, praise His ho - ly name.
Am
D7/F♯
Gm
C7
B♭
F
8va

Where No One Stands Alone

M. L.

MOSIE LISTER
Arr. by Ken Thomas

REFRAIN
C F Dm7 G7 C G7
hand all the way, ev - 'ry hour, ev - 'ry day, From here to the
Am G7/B C F
great un - known. Take my
C G7 Am F C G7
hand, let me stand Where no one stands a -
1 C Am Dm7 G7sus G7
lone. 2. Like a
2 C Am Dm7/F Fm/D C
lone.

All My Life

R. C. RALPH CARMICHAEL

Emadd 11 Em7 A13/9 A9 G/A DM7
Take a-way the doubt that hides Thy per - fect will.
G9sus G13 Co C7 C7sus Gm7 C7
Give me faith, in - stead, and with Thy Spir - it fill. Then
FM7 Gm11/F Gm9/F FM7 F6 F Cm7/B♭ F/C
all my days be the guard-ian of my ways; And I'll know the
G9/B B♭m9 B♭m/C C7 C7/F F Fsus B♭/D F/C
glo - ry of all Thy love thro' all my days. And I'll know the
G9/B B♭m9 B♭m/C C7 C7/F F
glo - ry of all Thy love thro' all my days.

I've Discovered the Way of Gladness

He Died for Us

J. O.

JIMMY OWENS
Arr. by Ken Thomas

1
2
Am
D7
There once stood a wall deep and
Man, by His blood, broke the
Bm
Em
Am
D
C/D
D7
wide, strong and tall. There it stood, built of all our un-
wall, loosed the flood Of the mer - cies of God to man-
1
G
Dm7
G
2
B7sus
B
8va
ho - li - ness. But this kind.
Em
Em/D♯
Em/D
F♯7/C♯
And now God of-fers to each one A price-less pardon for what we've done,
CM7
B7
Em
8va
Be-cause of Je - sus, His own Son, who died for us.

Beautiful Savior

Anonymous
Tr. by Joseph A. Seiss

TOM FETTKE
Based on an Irish Folk Song
Arr. by Ken Thomas

B
E
C♯m
A M7
2. Fair are the mead - ows; Fair are the
B
B sus
B
G♯m
A
F♯m
F♯m7
wood - lands, Robed in flow'rs of bloom - ing
B
B sus
B
E
C♯m
A M7
spring. Je - sus is fair - er; Je - sus is
B
B sus
B
G♯m
A
F♯m
F♯m7/B
B13
pur - er; He makes our sor - row - ing spir - its
E
C7
F
Dm
sing! 3. Beau - ti - ful Sav - ior,

Gm9 C7 Am7 Dm7 Gm7 C7
Lord of the na - tions, Son of God and Son of
F F7sus F7 B Gm Cm9
Man! Glo - ry and hon - or, Praise, ad - o -
F7sus F7 Dm7 E♭ B♭/D Cm7 B♭/D E♭ Gm/E
ra - tion, Now and for - ev - er, for - ev - er - more be
F7 Gm Dm/F E♭ Cm7 B♭/F F7sus F7
Thine! Now and for - ev - er - more be
B♭ Gm E♭ Cm F B♭
8va
Thine!

He Is the Way

(He Is the Truth; He Is the Life)

O. S. OTIS SKILLINGS

1-4
5
Bb C7 F Bb F/A Gm7 F F
TRUTH; HE IS THE LIFE.
2. 'Twas Je - sus
3. He gave His LIFE.
4. Rose from the
5. He lives to -
D7 G C/G G B/F# Em Dm6
f God sent His Son to be our Sav - ior; God sent His
C G/B Am7 A#o G/B G#o D7/A C C/G
Son to be our Sav - ior; God sent His Son
G B/F# Em C G Em
to be our Sav - ior. HE IS THE WAY; HE IS THE
Am7sus D7/F# G
8va
TRUTH; HE IS THE LIFE.
8va

The Lighthouse

R. H. RONNIE HINSON

REFRAIN
C G G7 C G13 F/C C F
And I thank God for the light - house; I owe my
G7 C G13 F/C C
life to Him. For Je - sus is the light - house, and
D9 G G7 C G13
from the rocks of sin He has shone a light a -
F/C C F G7 C G7 C G13
round me that I could clear - ly see. If it was - n't for the
C G7 F/G G7 1 C 2 C
light - house, (tell me,) where would this ship be? 2. Ev - 'ry - be?

Led by the Master's Hand

M. L.

MOSIE LISTER

C/G Am7 G7 G7sus C E♭°
led by the Mas - ter's hand.
led by the Mas - ter's hand.
Through the
CHORUS
G7/D G7 G13 C F♯° C/G C F♯°/A G7
storm, through the night, I'll keep hold - ing on. With His hand hold-ing
E/G♯ Am D7 G7 C C+
mine, hope is nev - er gone. When I climb the last mile to heav-en's
F A7 Dm F♯° C/G Am G7 G7sus
land, I'll be led by the Mas - ter's
1 F/C Fm6/C C G7
hand. 2. Through the
2 C F/C Fm6/C C
hand.

Jesus Will Be What Makes it Heaven for Me

L. W. | LANNY WOLFE

CHORUS
Ab
Ab/Eb
Eb
Heav - en for me, heav - en for me;
Cm7
F7
Bb7
Je - sus will be what makes it heav - en for me. All its
Eb
Eb7/Db
Ab6/C
C7/E
Fm
beau - ty and won - ders I'm long - ing to see; But
Gm
Ab6
Eb/Bb
Fm7/Bb
Bb7
1
Eb
Je - sus will be what makes it heav - en for me.
Bb9sus
2
Eb
Ab/Eb
Eb
2. If me.

The Day He Wore My Crown

P. J.

PHIL JOHNSON

C
D/E
Em
D/E
Em7
G/F
F M7
G sus
G
G7
p
mp
p
my crown.
C
F/C
C
F/C C
Dm7
mf
ff
my crown.
He could have called
His ho - ly
G sus
G
C M7
C6
C M7
C6
Dm7
Fa - ther
and said, "Take Me a-way,
please;
take
Me a-way."
He could have said,
D.C. al Coda
G sus
G
Am add 9
Am/G
F M7
G sus
G7
"I'm not
guilt - y
and I'm
not gon-na stay,
I'm not gon-na pay."
CODA
F M7
C/E
Dm7
C/G
G#o
my crown.

I'm the one to blame; I caused all the
pain. He gave him-self the day He wore my crown.
molto rit.
Come, Let Us Reason
K. M.
KEN MEDEMA
"Come, let us rea-son to-geth-er," that's what

A7sus A7 D D/C♯ Bm
God says. "Come, let us rea - son to -
Em9 A7 3rd time to Coda 1 D G/A A7 2 D
geth - er," says the Lord. Lord.
G F♯m Bm Em A9
"Though your sins be as scar - let, they shall be as
DM7 D7 G 3 Em6 F♯m Bm
white as snow; Though they be red like crim - son,
E9 A9sus A7 D.S. al Coda CODA D
they shall be as wool." Lord.

170

Jesus Is Lord of All

WILLIAM J. and GLORIA GAITHER

WILLIAM J. GAITHER

Dm/C C7 F C7/G F/A Bb
Lord of all. All my pos - ses - sions and
F C7 Dm/C C7
all my life, Je - sus is Lord of
1 F Bb/F 2 F Am7 D7
all. all.
G Am D/F♯ Am
3. All of my long - ings, all my dreams, Je - sus is
D7/F♯ Em D7 G C/G G
Lord of all. All of my fail - ures His

Am E♯o D/F♯ Am D7/F♯ Em D7
pow - er re - deems; Je - sus is Lord of
REFRAIN
G Dm7 G7 C G
all. King of kings, Lord of
D7 Em/D D7 G D7/A G/B
lords, Je - sus is Lord of all.
C G D7
All my pos - ses - sions and all my life, Je - sus is
Em/D D7 G C/G D/G G
Lord of all.

All Day Song

J. F. JOHN FISCHER

Dm7 C G
prom - is - es to stay.
1. When you think you got to
2. When He went a - way to
C G
wor - ry
heav - en,
'cause it seems the thing to
said He still has work to
C G
do,
do,
Re - mem - ber He ain't in a hur-
The Fa - ther has some ex - tra man-
Am F G
- ry;
- sions;
He's al - ways got time for you.
He's sav - in' one for you.
CODA
Dm7 C C/B♭ A♭ E♭/G
prom - is - es to stay.
Love Him in the morn - in' when you

Fm7
E♭
A♭
E♭/G
see the sun a - ris - in'.
Love Him in the eve - nin' 'cause He
took you through the day.
And in the in - be - tween time when you
feel the pres - sure com - in',
Re - mem - ber that He loves you and He
1
2
B♭7
prom - is - es to stay.
prom - is - es to
A♭/E♭
stay.

He Turned the Water into Wine

D. S.

DAVID STEARMAN

G D7/G G D7/G G D7/G G D7/G

G Am/G D/G G D7/G Am7 D7/A

1. He is the spar-kle in the snow ___ in the morn - ing
2. So set your fac-es to the sun, ___ for the sun did

G D7/G G Am/G D/G G D7/G

light; The ver-y warmth of fire's ___ glow ___ on a
rise. He's out to shine for ev-'ry-one; ___ o-pen

Am7 D7/A G D7/G Bm C Dsus D

win - ter night.
up your eyes.
And when He put His hand in

F
1
C
D7
G
D7/G
He turned the wa - ter in - to wine.
G
D7/G
G
D7/G
G
D7/G
2
C
D7
G
D7/G
G
C
D
He turned the wa - ter in - to wine.
He turned the wa - ter in - to
G
D7/G
G
C
D
Em
wine.
He turned the wa - ter in - to wine.
F
C
G
rit.

We Are Persuaded

W. J. G., G. G., and D. McG. — WILLIAM J. and GLORIA GAITHER and DONY McGUIRE

Gm
C7
Cm7
B♭/D
And who con - demns him, by God's own
And through our weak - ness, His might - y
E♭
E♭/F
F7
Gm
C7
Son has been for - giv - en? By hope we're driv - en,
pow'r is speak - ing. In pain there's sing - ing,
F
F/E
Dm
Gm
by grace for - giv - en; We're called by pur-
in death no sting - ing. Of this we're cer-
C7
Cm7
B♭/D
E♭
E♭/F
- pose to be spent for ser - vice.
- tain: through ev - 'ry-thing His love is work - in'!
N.C.
F7
B♭7
D.S. twice
CODA
Cm7
Cm7/F
B♭
We are per - rate us from His love.

I Want to Be like Jesus

THOMAS O. CHISHOLM

DAVID LIVINGSTON IVES

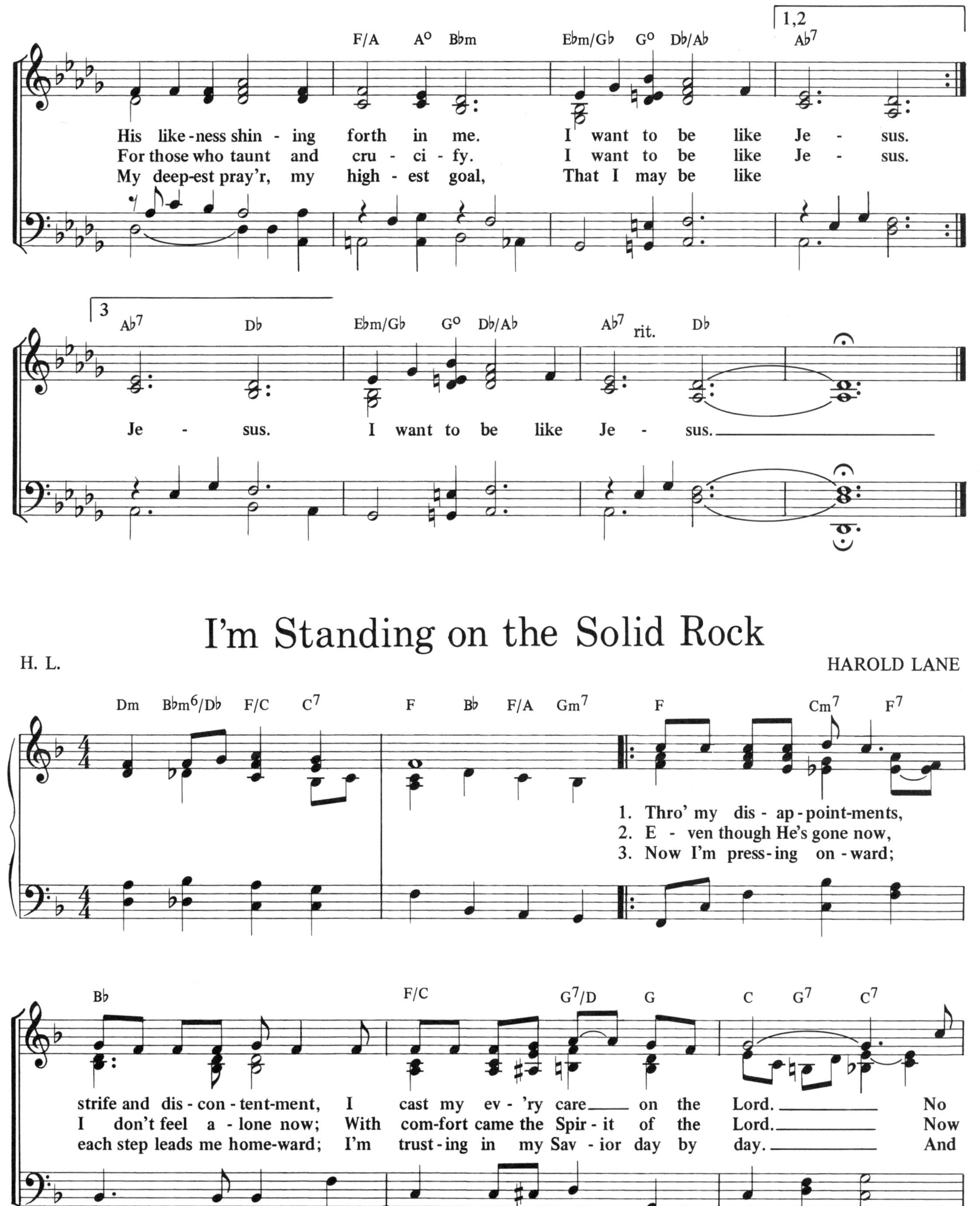
1,2
F/A A° Bbm Ebm/Gb G° Db/Ab Ab7
His like-ness shin - ing forth in me. I want to be like Je - sus.
For those who taunt and cru - ci - fy. I want to be like Je - sus.
My deep-est pray'r, my high - est goal, That I may be like
3
Ab7 Db Ebm/Gb G° Db/Ab Ab7 rit. Db
Je - sus. I want to be like Je - sus.
I'm Standing on the Solid Rock
H. L.
HAROLD LANE
Dm Bbm6/Db F/C C7 F Bb F/A Gm7 F Cm7 F7
1. Thro' my dis - ap - point-ments,
2. E - ven though He's gone now,
3. Now I'm press-ing on - ward;
Bb F/C G7/D G C G7 C7
strife and dis - con - tent-ment, I cast my ev - 'ry care on the Lord. No
I don't feel a - lone now; With com-fort came the Spir - it of the Lord. Now
each step leads me home-ward; I'm trust - ing in my Sav - ior day by day. And

F Cm7 F7 B♭
mat - ter what ob - ses - sion, pain, or deep de - pres - sion, I'm
with His Word to guide me, from temp - ta - tions hide me, I'm
close is our re - la - tion, firm is its foun - da - tion; So
CHORUS
F Dm B♭m6/D♭ F/C C7 F B♭ F C7 F F sus
stand - ing on the sol - id Rock.
stand - ing on the sol - id Rock. I'm stand - ing on the
on this sol - id Rock I'll stay.
F C7 F
Rock of A - ges, Safe from all the storm that ra - ges;
F sus F C♯o Dm F/C Dm B♭m6/D♭ F/C C7
Rich, but not from Sa - tan's wa - ges, I'm stand-ing on the sol - id
1,2
F B♭ F/A Gm7
Rock.
3
F F7 B♭/F B♭m/F F
Rock.

It Won't Be Long

A. C.

ANDRAÉ CROUCH

Slowly, with expression

Dm7 Gm7 Cm7 | F Gm F7/A E♭/B♭ | B♭ | Dm7 Gm7 Cm7

It won't be long,

F Gm F7/A E♭/B♭ | B♭ | Dm7 Gm7 Cm7

then we'll be leav - ing here. It won't be long,

F F7 | 1 B♭ Cm7

we'll be go - in' home.

2 B♭ Cm7/B♭ | B♭ | E♭ Cm7

home. Count the years as months,

F7
Bb
Cm
Dm
Bb7
Eb6
And count the months as weeks,
And count the weeks as days. An-y
F
F7
1 Bb
Cm7/Bb
2 Bb
day now
we'll be go - in' home.
home.
Bb
Bb7
Eb/Bb
Bb
Bb7
Eb/Bb
Bb
Bb7
Eb/Bb
Bb
Bb7
Eb/Bb
Spoken: Beloved, now we are the sons of God, and it doth not yet appear what we shall be: but we know
Bb
Bb7
Eb/Bb
Bb
Bb7
Eb
when Christ shall appear, we shall be like Him; for we shall see Him just as He is, in all of His splendor and

B♭ B♭7 E♭ B♭ B♭7 E♭
glory! In all of His righteousness, Jesus Christ, the Son of God. (Sing) We shall be like Him;
F F7/E♭ B♭/D Cm7 F B♭ B♭7 E♭ Cm7
We shall be like Him; We shall be like Him. An-y day now
F F7 B♭ Cm7 Dm7 Gm7 Cm7
we'll be go - in' home. It won't be long,
F Gm F7/A E♭/B♭ B♭ Dm7 Gm7 Cm7
then we'll be leav - ing here. It won't be long,
F F7 B♭ Dm7 Cm7 F7 B♭
we'll be go - in' home. rit.

Praise the Lord

B. B. and M. H.

BROWN BANNISTER and MIKE HUDSON

Am E+ Am7 D Am7 D
Lord! For the chains that seem to bind you serve on - ly to re-mind you that they drop
C/E D/F♯ 3rd time to Coda G sus 1 G D C/D 2 G C/G D.S. al Coda
pow-er-less be-hind you when you praise Him. 2. Now Him Praise the
CODA
G sus G G/F C/E
praise Him, praise Him, praise Him; When you
Cm add9 Eb Cm/Eb G/D A/C♯
praise Him, when you praise Him; When you
C Am D sus C/D G sus G
praise the Lord.
rit.
8va

The Love of God

F. M. L. | F. M. LEHMAN

Ab Bb Gm Cm7 Fm Bb9 Eb Ab Bb
God, how rich and pure! How meas-ure - less and strong! It shall for - ev - er-more en-
Gm Cm7 Fm Bb13 1 Eb Bb7sus 2 Eb
dure the saints' and an - gels' song. 2. When hoar-y song.
3. Could we with
Ten Thousand Angels
R. O.
RAY OVERHOLT
Rubato
C C/E G7 C
1. They bound the hands of Je - sus in the gar - den where He prayed; They
(2. Up -) on His pre-cious head they placed a crown of thorns; They
(3. When they) nailed Him to the cross, His moth - er stood near - by; He
(4. To the) howl-ing mob He yield - ed; He did not for mer - cy cry. The

F
C
G7/D
C
led Him through the streets in shame.
laughed and said, "Be - hold the King."
said, "Wom-an, be - hold thy son!"
cross of shame He took a - lone.
They spat up - on the Sav - ior, so
They struck Him and they cursed Him and
He cried, "I thirst for wa - ter," but they
And when He cried, "It's fin - ished," He
G
C
Dm7
G13
C
REFRAIN
Dm C/E
pure and free from sin. They said, "Cru - ci - fy Him! He's to blame."
mock'd His ho - ly name. All a - lone He suf-fered ev - 'ry - thing.
gave Him none to drink. Then the sin - ful work of man was done.
gave him - self to die. Sal - va - tion's won-drous plan was done.
He could have
Faster, in tempo
F
C
G7
called ten thou - sand an - gels To de-stroy the world and set Him
C
G7/C
C
C7/E
F
C
free. He could have called ten thou - sand an - gels, But He died a -
G7/D
C
G7
1-3
C
4
C
F/C
C
lone for you and me.
2. Up
3. When they
4. To the
me.

Oh, How He Loves You and Me

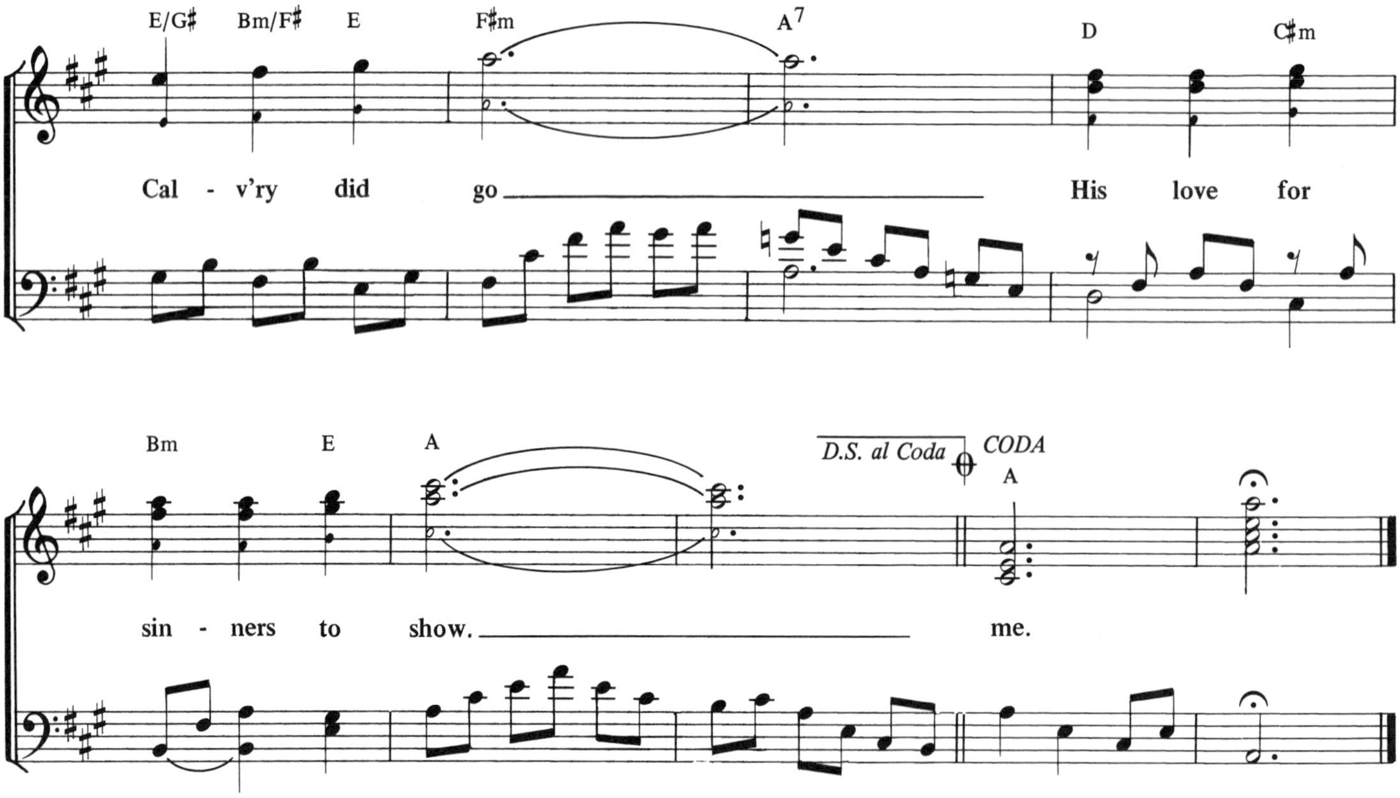
E/G♯ Bm/F♯ E F♯m A7 D C♯m
Cal - v'ry did go His love for
Bm E A
D.S. al Coda
CODA
A
sin - ners to show. me.

Shepherd of Love

J. W. P.

JOHN W. PETERSON

D D♯o Em A D D♯o Em A D D♯o
simile
Shep - herd of
Em A7 A7sus A7 D D D♯o
Love, You knew I had lost my way; Shep - herd of

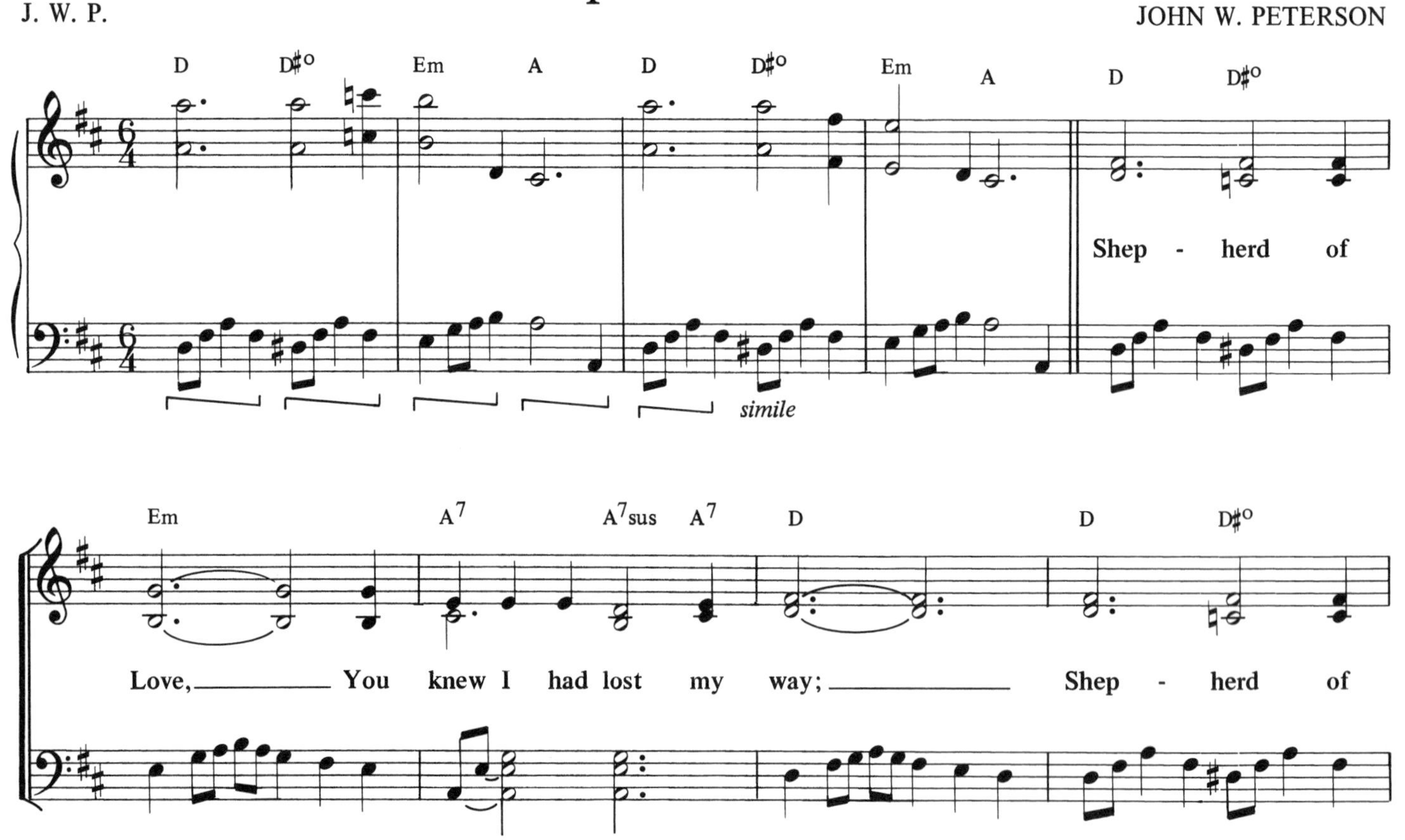

Em
A7
D
D7
G
G♯o
love, You cared that I'd gone a - stray. You sought and found me,
D/A
B7
Em
A7
D
D7
G
G♯o
placed a - round me strong arms that car - ried me home. No foe can harm me
D/A
A7
B7
Em
E7
Em7/A
A7
D
D♯o
or a - larm me; Nev - er a - gain will I roam! Shep - herd of
Em
A
A sus
A
D
D
D♯o
Love, Sav - ior and Lord and Guide; Shep - herd of
Em
A7
D
G/D
D
Love, For - ev - er I'll stay by Your side.

His Hand in Mine

M. L. MOSIE LISTER

B♭/F
F
C
D9
D
walk a - lone; He holds my hand.
He will guide each step I take, and
Am7
D13
G7
A♯o
G7/B
G7
if I fall I know He'll un - der - stand.
'Til the day He tells my why He loves me
When the time shall come to leave this world be-
C
F/G
C
1
G7
G9
C/G
G6
G7
C
so,
hind,
I can feel His hand in mine; that's all I need to know.
I will walk that
2
G7
G9
C/G
E/G♯
Am
2. Oth - er friends that
lone - some val - ley with His hand in mine.
D9
G7
G9
C/G
G6
G7
C
I will walk that lone - some val - ley with His hand in mine.

Say "I Do"

R. H.

RAY HILDEBRAND

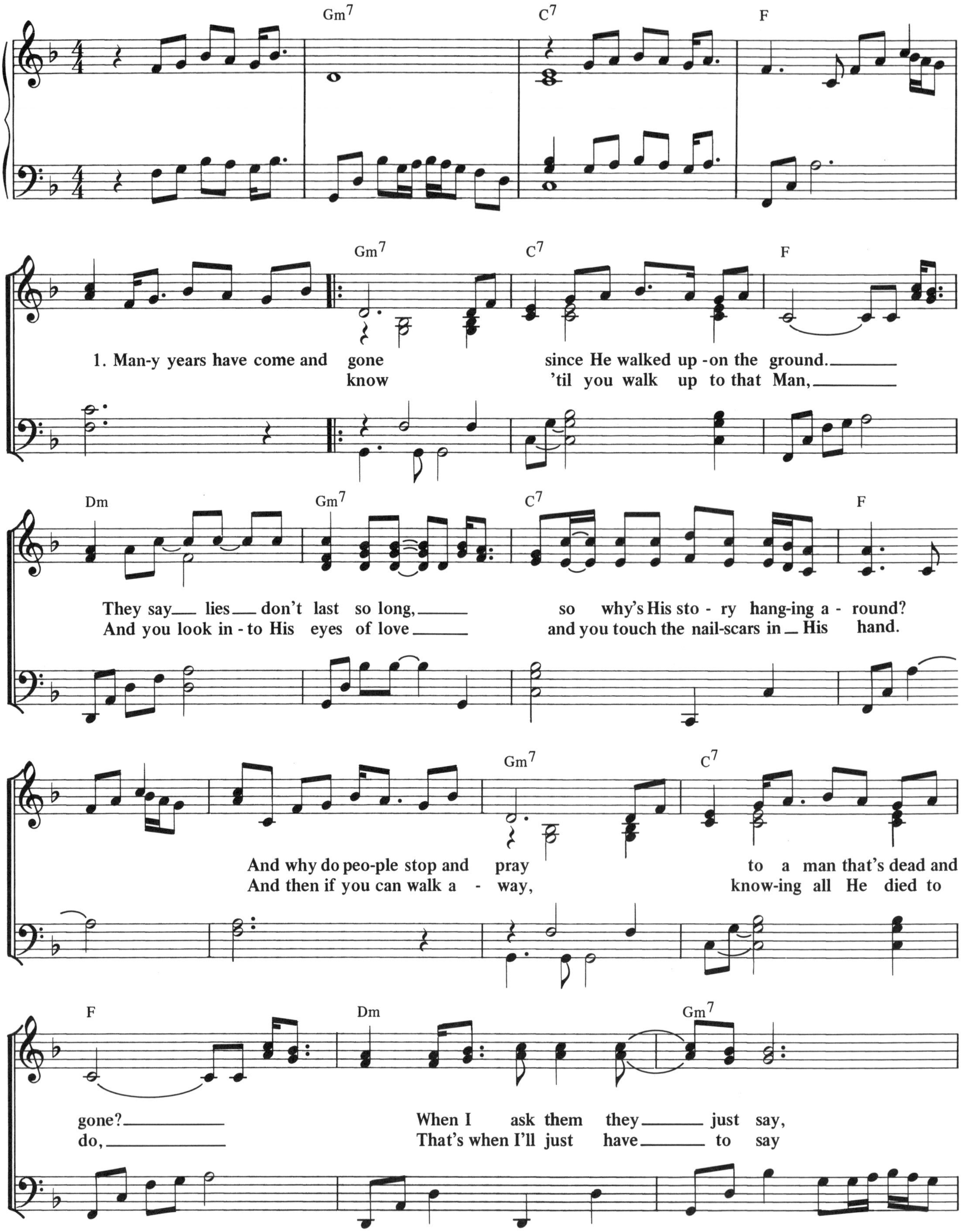
Gm7
C7
F
Gm7
C7
F
1. Man-y years have come and gone since He walked up-on the ground.
know 'til you walk up to that Man,
Dm
Gm7
C7
F
They say lies don't last so long, so why's His sto-ry hang-ing a-round?
And you look in-to His eyes of love and you touch the nail-scars in His hand.
Gm7
C7
And why do peo-ple stop and pray to a man that's dead and
And then if you can walk a-way, know-ing all He died to
F
Dm
Gm7
gone? When I ask them they just say,
do, That's when I'll just have to say

C7
F
E♭add9 B♭
F
Gm7
"He's com-ing back to take me home."
I guess He did-n't die_ for you.
An-y-bod-y here want to live for ev - er, say "I
C7
F F sus F
F
do." An-y-bod-y here want-a walk on golden streets, say "I do." Anybody here sick and tired of
Gm7
F
Dm7
Gm7
C7
liv - in' like you do;
An-y-bod-y here want a home with love for - ev - er, say "I
1
F Dm7 Gm7 C7 F
2
F Dm7
do."
2. And they say you will never do."
Gm7 C7 F Dm7 Gm7 C7 F
Say "I do."

He Looked Beyond My Fault

DOTTIE RAMBO

Adapted from Londonderry Aire

Fm/A♭ C/G Dm/G G C

F/G CM7 C6 Gm Gm6 F

A - maz - ing grace shall al - ways be my song of praise,

Dm7 Fm Em Am7 D7/A G7sus

For it was grace that bought my lib - er - ty.

G Fm/G CM7 C6 Gm7 Gm6 F

I do not know just why He came to love me so;

Fm C Dm9 F/G G C

He looked be - yond my fault and saw my need.

REFRAIN
G
C
F
Em
Dm7
C
I shall for - ev - er lift mine eyes to Cal - va - ry,
F/G
G
Am
F
C
D7/A
To view the cross where Je - sus died for me.
G7
Em
G/D
C
C+
F
F
E/G♯
How mar - vel - ous the grace that caught my fall - ing
Am
Am/G
D9/F♯
Fm/A♭
C/G
2nd time to Coda
F/G
G
soul; He looked be - yond my fault and saw my
C
F/G
CM7
C6
C7
need. A - maz - ing grace shall al - ways be my

F
Dm7
G13
Em
Am7
D7
song of praise, For it was grace that bought my lib - er -
Dm7/G
G
Fm/G
C M7
C6
C9
ty. I do not know just why He came to
F
Fm6
Fm
C
Dm9
F/G
G9
love me so; He looked be - yond my fault and saw my
D.S. al Coda
CODA
C
F/G
G
C
D9/F♯
Fm/A♭
need. I shall for - need.
C/G
Dm/G
G13
C

It Is Finished

WILLIAM J. and GLORIA GAITHER

WILLIAM J. GAITHER

F♯ F♯/A♯ B
dev - ils of hell. On the oth-er the an - gels of
E/B B F♯7 F♯7/A♯ B B/A
glo - ry; And they meet on Gol - go - tha's hill.
G C Dm7 C/E F
3. The earth shakes with the force of the con-flict And the
my heart the bat - tle was rag - ing; Not all
heard that the King of the a - ges Had
C Dm7 C/E Dm7 G C
sun re - fus - es to shine, For there hangs God's
pris - ner's of war had come home. They were bat-tle-fields of
fought all the bat - tles for me; And vic - t'ry was
C7sus C7 F C G F/G G7
Son in the bal - ance; And then through the dark - ness He
my own mak - ing, Did-n't know that the war had been
mine for the claim - ing; And now, praise His name, I am

2 | 1,3

C Dm7/C C Dm7/G C C Dm7 C/E

won. 5. Then I cries, free. "It is fin-ished"; the bat - tle is

f

F C C G7/C C G7

o - ver. "It is fin-ished"; There'll be no more war.

G13 F C F/C C *2nd time to Coda*

"It is fin - ished"; the end of the con - flict. "It is fin-ished," and

Dm/G G7 C Dm7/C *D.S.* *CODA* Dm/G G13

Je - sus is Lord! 4. Yet in Je - sus is

p

Ab Fm C

Lord. rit.

Spirit Song

J. W.

JOHN WIMBER

REFRAIN
G
Em7
A7
F♯m7
Bm7
Je - sus, O Je - sus,
Em7
A7
D M7
D9
come and fill Your lambs;
G
Em7
A7
A9/G
F♯m7
Bm7
Je - sus, O Je - sus,
Em7
A9
D
1
A7/E
D7/F♯
come and fill Your lambs.
2. O come and
2
Bm
D/A
Em7
A7
A13
G/A
D
He'll de - scend up-on your life and make you whole.

Through It All

A. C.

ANDRAÉ CROUCH

REFRAIN
Eb
Ab
Through it all, through it all, Oh, I've
Bb7
Ab/Bb
Eb
learned to trust in Je - sus; I've learned to trust in God.
Cm/A
Through it all, through it all, I've
Bb7sus
1,2
learned to de - pend up - on His Word.
3
F7
rit.
Word. Oh, I've learned to de - pend up - on His Word.

I Am Loved

WILLIAM J. and GLORIA GAITHER

WILLIAM J. GAITHER

F
C7
I said, "If You knew, You would-n't want me; My
giv-en, I re - peat it, I'm for - giv - en; And
Gm7
Bb/C
C7
F
Bb/C
C
Bb/C
C7
scars are hid-den by the face I wear."
clean be-fore my Lord I free - ly stand. For-
F
Cm7
F7
Eb/Bb
Bb
Gm7
He said, "My child, My scars go deep - er;
giv-en, I can dare for-give my broth - er. For-
C7
Gm7
C7
F
Bb/C
D.S. two times
It was love for you that put them there."
giv - en, I reach out to take your hand.
I am
CODA
F
Bb/C
F
Bb/C
F
loved.

In His Time

D. B.
Based on Eccles. 3:11

DIANE BALL

F♯m7 B7 E A/E E
time, in Your time; You make
F♯m F♯m7♯ F♯m7 B9 E E7
all things beau - ti - ful in Your time. Lord, my
A B/A G♯m7 C♯m C♯m7
life to You I bring; May each song I have to sing Be to
F♯m7 B7 E
You a love - ly thing in Your time.
A/E E A/E E
rit.

Index